CW00408695

MASTERING MATHEMATICS

ALGEBRA

Series Editor: Roger Porkess

HODDER
EDUCATION
AN HACHETTE UK COMPANY

Series contributors:

Bola Adiboye, Caroline Clissold, Ruth Crookes, Heather Davis, Paul Dickinson, Alan Easterbrook, Sarah-Anne Fernandes, Dave Gale, Sophie Goldie, Steve Gough, Kevin Higham, Sue Hough, Andrew Jeffrey, Michael Kent, Donna Kerrigan, Nigel Langdon, Linda Liggett, Robin Liggett, Andrew Manning, Nikki Martin, Chris Messenger, Richard Perring, Grahame Smart, Alison Terry, Sam Webber, Colin White

Some activities from Formula One Maths, used with permission of authors

Some SMILE activities © RBKC, used with permission

The Publishers would like to thank the following for permission to reproduce copyright material:

Photo credits:

p.2 © Coprid – Fotolia.com; **p.19** Juri Samsonov – Fotolia.com; **p.26** © olgataranik – Fotolia.com; **p.35** © Warren Goldswain – Fotolia.com; **p.47** © klikk – Fotolia.com; **p.56** © picsfive – Fotolia.com; **p.64** © Corbis/ Education - image100 RFCD697; **p.71** © RTimages – Fotolia.com; **p.78** © Claudio Divizia – Fotolia.com; **p.100** © pathakdesigner – Fotolia.com; **p.118** © GaryBartlett - Thinkstock; **p.126** © Britain On View/VisitBritain / Britain 100 CD001RF; **p.134** © Photodisc/ Getty Images/Retail, Shopping and Small Business 21; **p.154** © Ingram Publishing Company / Ultimate Business 06; **p.164** © Kautz15 -Fotolia.com; **p.178** © GoodMood Photo – Fotolia.com; **p.188** © The Photos – Fotolia.com; **p.196** © Ingram Publishing Limited / Ingram Image Library 500-Food; **p.206** © bloomua – Fotolia.com; **p.212** © alanstenson – Fotolia.com; **p. 222** © MADDRAT – Fotolia.com

Although every effort has been made to ensure that website addresses are correct at time of going to press, Hodder Education cannot be held responsible for the content of any website mentioned. It is sometimes possible to find a relocated web page by typing in the address of the home page for a website in the URL window of your browser.

Orders: please contact Bookpoint Ltd, 130 Milton Park, Abingdon, Oxon OX14 4SB.
Telephone: (44) 01235 827720. Fax: (44) 01235 400454. Lines are open 9.00–17.00, Monday to Saturday, with a 24-hour message answering service.
Visit our website at www.hoddereducation.co.uk

© Hodder & Stoughton 2014

First published in 2014 by

Hodder Education
An Hachette UK Company,
Carmelite House, 50 Victoria Embankment
London EC4Y 0DZ

Impression number	5	4	
Year	2018	2017	2016

Cover photo © fffranz – Fotolia

Typeset in 10/11.5pt ITC Avant Garde Gothic by Integra Software Services Pvt. Ltd., Pondicherry, India

Printed in Italy

A catalogue record for this title is available from the British Library

ISBN 978 1471 805790

This book covers the Algebra that you need for your key stage 3 Maths course.

The material is split into **four strands**:

- Starting algebra
- Sequences
- Functions and graphs
- Algebraic methods

Each strand is presented as a series of units that get more difficult as you progress (from Band b through to Band h). In total there are 24 units in this book.

Getting started

At the beginning of each strand, you will find a 'Progression strand flowchart'. It shows what skills you will develop in each unit in the strand. You can see:

- what you need to know before starting each unit
- what you will need to learn next to progress

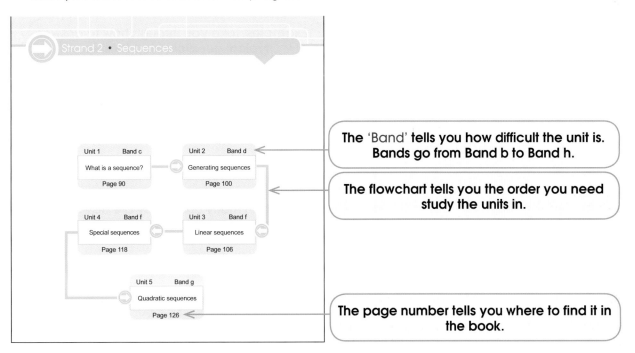

When you start to use this book, you will need to identify where to join each strand. Then you will not spend time revisiting skills you have already mastered.

If you can answer all the questions in the 'Reviewing skills' section of a unit then you will not have to study that unit.

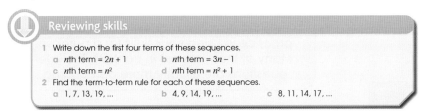

Reviewing skills

1. Write down the first four terms of these sequences.
   a. nth term = $2n + 1$
   b. nth term = $3n - 1$
   c. nth term = n^2
   d. nth term = $n^2 + 1$
2. Find the term-to-term rule for each of these sequences.
   a. 1, 7, 13, 19, ...
   b. 4, 9, 14, 19, ...
   c. 8, 11, 14, 17, ...

When you know which unit to start with in each strand you will be ready to start work on your first unit.

Starting a unit

Every unit begins with a 'Building skills' section:

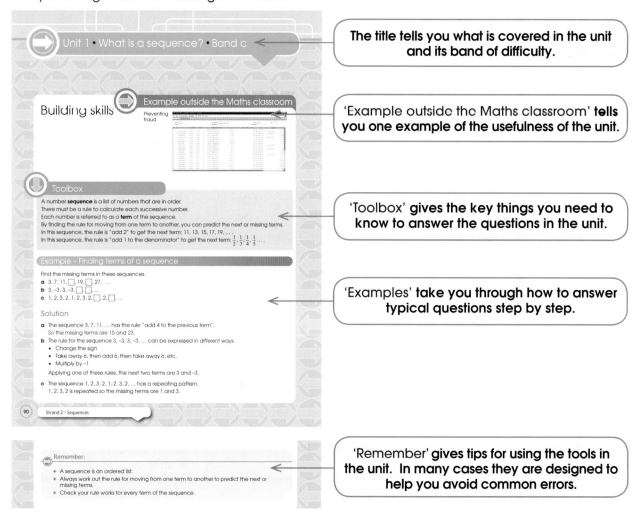

The title tells you what is covered in the unit and its band of difficulty.

'Example outside the Maths classroom' tells you one example of the usefulness of the unit.

'Toolbox' gives the key things you need to know to answer the questions in the unit.

'Examples' take you through how to answer typical questions step by step.

'Remember' gives tips for using the tools in the unit. In many cases they are designed to help you avoid common errors.

Now you have all the information you need, you can use the questions to develop your understanding.

Skills practice A

1 Bob is two years older than Pete.
   a Who is older?
   b Which of these rules is correct?
      i Bob's age + 2 = Pete's age
      ii Pete's age + 2 = Bob's age

2 The CD of a song costs twice as much as the download.
   Which of these rules is correct?
      i Cost of CD × 2 = cost of download
      ii Cost of download ÷ 2 = cost of CD
      iii Cost of download × 2 = cost of CD

'Skills practice A' questions are all about mastering essential techniques that you need to succeed.

Skills practice B

1 Jean is paid £4 per hour more than Ken.
   a Copy and complete this formula

      Jean's hourly wage in pounds = Ken's hourly wage in pounds ☐

   b Ken uses a different formula that shows the same information.
      Copy and complete Ken's formula.

      Ken's hourly wage in pounds = ☐

   c Jean is paid £16 per hour.
      How much is Ken paid?
      Use these amounts to check that your formulae are correct.

2 An online discount store is having a half price sale.
   Some of these formulae are correct. Which are they?
   a Sale price = Regular price × 2
   b Sale price = Regular price ÷ 2
   c Regular price = Sale price × 2
   d Regular price ÷ Sale price = 2
   e Sale price ÷ Regular price = 2

'Skills practice B' questions give you practice in using your skills for a purpose. Many of them are set in context. The later questions are usually more demanding.

Wider skills practice

1 Jack is writing down some formulae to do with time.

    Number of seconds = number of minutes × 60

    Number of weeks = number of days ÷ 7

a How many seconds are there in four minutes?
b Jack's brother has 28 days' holiday each year.
    How many weeks is this?
c Copy and complete this formula

    Number of days = Number of weeks ☐

    Jack's sister has 3 weeks' holiday in her job.
    How many days' holiday does she have?
d Copy and complete this formula

    Number of seconds = Number of weeks ☐

> **'Wider skills practice' questions require you to use maths from outside the current unit. In some cases they use knowledge from other subjects or the world outside.**
>
> **You can use this section to keep practising other skills as well as the skills in this unit.**

Applying skills

1 Samir has a formula for estimating the height of a person.

Measure round your head. Multiply your answer by 3. This gives your height.

Samir

a How tall is Becky?

Becky

b How tall are these people?

> **'Applying skills' questions give examples of how you will use the Maths in the unit to solve problems:**
> - **in the real world**
> - **in other subjects**
> - **in personal finance**
> - **within Maths itself.**
>
> **These are more demanding questions, so only one or two are provided in each unit. Together they form a bank of questions.**

When you feel confident, use the 'Reviewing skills' section to check that you have mastered the techniques covered in the unit.

You will see many questions labelled with (Reasoning) or (Problem solving)

These are the general mathematical skills that you need to develop. You will use these skills in all areas of Maths.

They will help you think through problems and to apply your skills in unfamiliar situations. Use these questions to make sure that you develop these important skills.

About 'Bands'

Every unit has been allocated to a Band. These bands show you the level of difficulty of the Maths that you are working on.

Each Band contains Maths that's of about the same level of difficulty.

This provides a way of checking your progress and assessing your weaker areas, where you need to practise more.

Moving on to another unit

Once you have completed a unit, you should move on to the next unit in one of the strands. You can choose which strand to work on next but make sure you complete all the units in a particular Band before moving on to the next Band.

A note for teachers

Bands have been assigned to units roughly in line with the previous National Curriculum levels. Here they are, just to help in giving you a reference point.

Band	Approximate Equivalent in terms of Old National Curriculum Levels
b	Level 2
c	Level 3
d	Level 4
e	Level 5
f	Level 6
g	Level 7
h	Level 8

Answers

Answers to all the questions in this book will be available via **Mastering Mathematics Teaching and Learning Resources** or by visiting **www.hodderplus.co.uk/masteringmaths**

Contents

Strand 1 Starting algebra — 01

Unit 1 Making and using word formulae — 02

Unit 2 Using letters — 10

Unit 3 Combining variables — 19

Unit 4 Working with formulae — 26

Unit 5 Setting up and solving simple equations — 35

Unit 6 Using brackets — 47

Unit 7 Working with more complex equations — 56

Unit 8 Solving equations with brackets — 64

Unit 9 Simplifying harder expressions — 71

Unit 10 Using complex formulae — 78

Strand 2 Sequences — 89

Unit 1 What is a sequence? — 90

Unit 2 Generating sequences — 100

Unit 3 Linear sequences — 106

Unit 4 Special sequences — 118

Unit 5 Quadratic sequences — 126

Strand 3 Functions and graphs — 133

Unit 1 Real-life graphs — 134

Unit 2 Plotting graphs of linear functions — 154

Unit 3 The equation of a straight line — 164

Unit 4 Plotting quadratic and cubic graphs — 178

Strand 4 Algebraic methods — 187

Unit 1 Trial and improvement — 188

Unit 2 Linear inequalities — 196

Unit 3 Solve pairs of equations by substitution — 206

Unit 4 Solve simultaneous equations using elimination — 212

Unit 5 Using graphs to solve simultaneous equations — 222

Strand 1 • Starting algebra

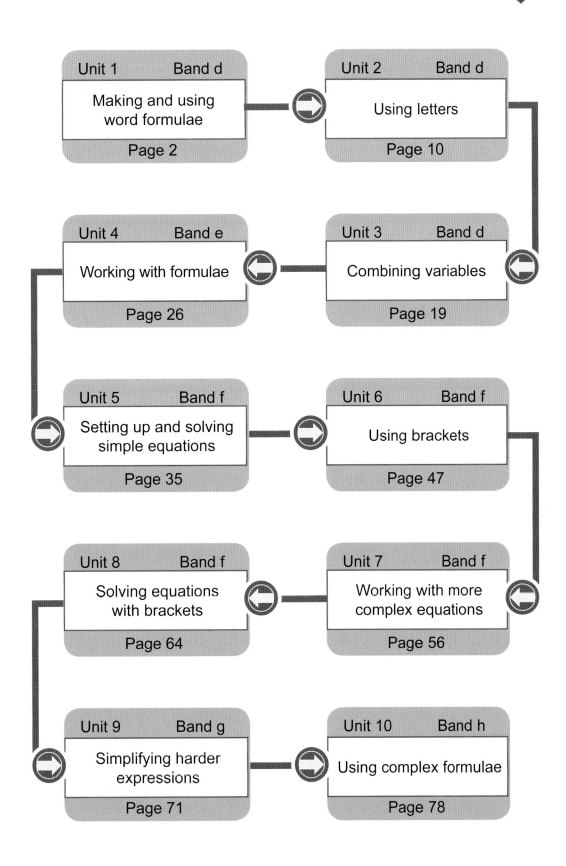

Unit 1	Band d
Making and using word formulae	
Page 2	

Unit 2	Band d
Using letters	
Page 10	

Unit 4	Band e
Working with formulae	
Page 26	

Unit 3	Band d
Combining variables	
Page 19	

Unit 5	Band f
Setting up and solving simple equations	
Page 35	

Unit 6	Band f
Using brackets	
Page 47	

Unit 8	Band f
Solving equations with brackets	
Page 64	

Unit 7	Band f
Working with more complex equations	
Page 56	

Unit 9	Band g
Simplifying harder expressions	
Page 71	

Unit 10	Band h
Using complex formulae	
Page 78	

Unit 1 · Making and using word formulae · Band d

Building skills

Example outside the Maths classroom

Heating a room

Toolbox

A **formula** is a rule for working something out:

　　　Dave's age = Sally's age – 4.

The same information can be shown using an equivalent formula:

　　　Sally's age = Dave's age + 4

　　　Sally's age – Dave's age = 4

The words in a formula can be replaced with numbers that you know.
This is called **substituting**.

If Sally is 16 then:

　　　Dave's age = Sally's age – 4

　　　Dave's age = 16 – 4

　　　Dave's age = 12

Example – Using a formula

The time needed to roast a turkey is 50 minutes plus an extra 30 minutes per kilogramme:

　　　Cooking time in minutes = 50 + 30 × mass in kg

What is the cooking time for a 5 kg turkey?

Solution

　　　Cooking time in minutes = 50 + 30 × mass in kg

　　　　　　　　　= 50 + 30 × 5

　　　　　　　　　= 50 + 150

　　　　　　　　　= 200 minutes

　　　　　　　　　= 3 hours 20 minutes

> **Substitute the mass of the turkey given into the formula.**

Example – Understanding a formula

Kevin uses a formula to work out the total points for each football team in his local league:

Total points = 3 × number of wins + number of draws

Explain why Kevin's formula works.

Solution

There are 3 points for every win.
The number of points for the wins is three times the number of wins.
There is 1 point for every draw.
The number of points for the draws is the same as the number of draws.
There are no points for a loss.
Kevin adds the points for wins and draws to find the total number of points.

Remember:

✦ The words in a formula must stand for numbers.
✦ The order of a formula must exactly match the order of the calculations it represents.
✦ It must be clear what units are being used.
✦ Always check the answer when you have used a formula to work something out to make sure that it is sensible.

Skills practice A

1 Bob is two years older than Pete.
   a Who is older?
   b Which of these rules is correct?

   i Bob's age + 2 = Pete's age
   ii Pete's age + 2 = Bob's age

2 The CD of a song costs twice as much as the download.
   Which of these rules is correct?

   i Cost of CD × 2 = cost of download
   ii Cost of download ÷ 2 = cost of CD
   iii Cost of download × 2 = cost of CD

3 Ali has 20 fewer books than Sally.
   a Who has more books?
   b Which of these rules is correct?

   i Number of Ali's books + number of Sally's books = 20
   ii Number of Ali's books + 20 = number of Sally's books
   iii Number of Ali's books – 20 = number of Sally's books

Reasoning

Reasoning

4 a What is the cost of

    i 2 apples

    ii 10 apples

    iii 20 apples

    iv 100 apples?

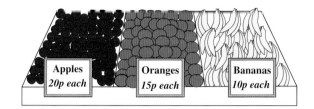

Apples	Oranges	Bananas
20p each	15p each	10p each

b Copy and complete this formula.

    Cost in pence = number of apples × ☐

5 Look at this advert.

SPEEDY BOATS
£5 per hour

a Copy and complete this formula.

    Cost of hire (£) = ☐ × number of hours

b Work out the cost to hire a boat for

    i 2 hours   **ii** 3 hours   **iii** 12 hours.

6 Here is part of a price list for hiring tools:

Item	Hire cost	Daily charge
Extension ladder	£10	£20
Wheelbarrow	£8	£20
Concrete mixer	£12	£30
Chainsaw	£15	£30
Nail gun	£4	£10
Circular saw	£6	£20

The hire shop uses this formula to work out the cost of hiring an extension ladder.

    total cost of hiring extension ladder = 10 + 20 × number of days hired

a Write a formula for hiring each of the other tools.

    i Total cost of hiring a wheelbarrow

    ii Total cost of hiring a concrete mixer

    iii Total cost of hiring a chainsaw

    iv Total cost of hiring a nail gun

    v Total cost of hiring a circular saw

b Use your formulae to work out the cost of hiring

    i a ladder for four days

    ii a wheelbarrow for two days

    iii a concrete mixer for one day

    iv a chainsaw for two days

    v a nail gun for a week

    vi a circular saw for two days.

c Dan is giving his garden a make-over at the weekend.
He needs a chainsaw, a concrete mixer and a wheelbarrow.
How much does it cost him to hire them all for two days?

Skills practice B

1 Jean is paid £4 per hour more than Ken.

   a Copy and complete this formula

      Jean's hourly wage in pounds = Ken's hourly wage in pounds ☐

   b Ken uses a different formula that shows the same information.
      Copy and complete Ken's formula.

      Ken's hourly wage in pounds = ☐

   c Jean is paid £16 per hour.
      How much is Ken paid?
      Use these amounts to check that your formulae are correct.

2 An online discount store is having a half price sale.
   Some of these formulae are correct. Which are they?

   a Sale price = Regular price × 2

   b Sale price = Regular price ÷ 2

   c Regular price = Sale price × 2

   d Regular price ÷ Sale price = 2

   e Sale price ÷ Regular price = 2

All items half price — Clearance *sale*

3 Jo and Raj are co-pilots in a jet that flies from London to New York.
   The journey is 3500 miles long.
   They share the flying.

   a Raj flies the first 2200 miles.
      How far does Jo fly?

   b On another trip, Jo flies 1800 miles.
      How far does Raj fly?

   c Copy and complete this formula.

      Distance flown by Raj = 3500 ☐

   d Write another formula that gives the same information in a different way.

4 A railway company works out its fares using this formula

      Divide the length of the journey in kilometres by 10 and then add 5.

   The answer is the fare in £.
   Find the fares for journeys of

   a 50 km   **b** 100 km

   c 200 km   **d** 5 km.

5 Jenny travels regularly on the motorway for her job.
   She says, 'I work out roughly how long a journey will take using this formula:

      Every 100 km takes 1 hour and every stop for a meal takes 1 hour.'

   How long does Jenny take on the following journeys?

   a 400 km with one meal   **b** 600 km with two meals   **c** 150 km with no meals

Reasoning

Wider skills practice

1 Jack is writing down some formulae to do with time.

> Number of seconds = number of minutes × 60
>
> Number of weeks = number of days ÷ 7

a How many seconds are there in four minutes?

b Jack's brother has 28 days' holiday each year.
How many weeks is this?

c Copy and complete this formula

Number of days = Number of weeks [   ]

Jack's sister has 3 weeks' holiday in her job.
How many days' holiday does she have?

d Copy and complete this formula

Number of seconds = Number of weeks [   ]

2 Kwame is working out the mean of some numbers.

a Use these words to write a formula to help him.

how many numbers there are	sum of all the numbers

mean

b Write two more formulae using these words that give the same information.

c Kwame works out the mean of 5, 8 and 14.
Use these numbers to check that your formulae are correct.

3 a What do the angles in a triangle add up to?

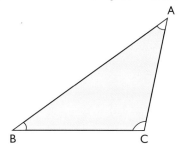

b Michelle starts to tell you a formula.
Copy and complete her formula.

Angle A + Angle ...

Michelle

4 Flyn is exploring right-angled triangles.

a What is the size of angle m?

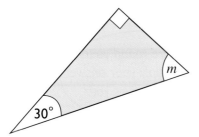

b Flyn has written this formula to find the angle p.

$$p = q + 90°$$

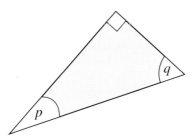

Flyn's formula doesn't work.
What should he have written?

c How many different formulae can you find that connect angles p and q?

5 Mark writes down this sequence.

Mark

a How does Mark work out the next number in his sequence?

b What is the tenth term in Mark's sequence?

c Copy and complete this formula for the value of the nth term in Mark's sequence.

nth term = ⬚ × term number

d Mercy changes Mark's sequence into 3, 5, 7, 9, 11, … .
What has she done?

e Write a formula for the nth term of Mercy's sequence.

f Write a formula for the nth term of the sequence 1, 3, 5, 7, 9, … .

Applying skills

1 Samir has a formula for estimating the height of a person.

Measure round your head. Multiply your answer by 3. This gives your height.

Samir

a How tall is Becky?

Becky

b How tall are these people?

c Does Samir's formula work?

Measure yourself and some friends to find out.

Problem solving

Reviewing skills

1 Look at this advert.

> **Mobile Phones**
> Calls cost 25p per minute

a Copy and complete this formula.

Cost (in pence) = [＿＿＿＿＿] × number of minutes

b What is the cost of a six-minute call?

2 The price of petrol has gone up again.

> **Petrol**
> **£2**
> **per litre**

a What is the cost of the following quantities of petrol?

  i 10 litres   ii 20 litres   iii 100 litres

b Copy and complete this formula.

Cost (in pounds) = number of litres × [＿＿＿＿＿]

3 Look at this advert.

> **Mad about Music**
>
> *CDs £12 each*
> *DVDs £15 each*

a Copy and complete this formula.

Price = [＿＿＿＿] × number of CDs + [＿＿＿＿] × number of DVDs

b Use the formula to work out the price of

  i 3 CDs   ii 2 DVDs   iii 2 CDs and 1 DVD   iv 4 CDs and 3 DVDs.

Building skills

Example outside the Maths classroom

Financial spreadsheets

	A	B	C	D	E
			D3	▾	f_x =B3*C3
1	Date	Hours worked	Rate per hour (£)	Total (£)	
2	23rd Sept	5	20	100	
3	25th Sept	6	25	150	
4	26th Sept	7.5	30	225	
5	27th Sept	4	25	100	
6	29th Sept	2	20	40	
7	30th Sept	4	15	60	
8	Total	28.5		675	
9					

Toolbox

A **formula** is a rule for working something out.

It is important to say what each of the letters in a formula stands for.

For example, in the formula, $W = 10h$

W means 'total wage in pounds' and h means 'number of hours worked'.

The letters stand for numbers. They are not abbreviations for words.

h = hours ✘

h = number of hours worked ✓

The letters used in a formula are called **variables**.

They represent numbers which can change (or vary).

In the formula $W = 10h$,

because there is no sign between the number and the variable, they should be multiplied.

$W = 10h$

When $h = 25$, $W = 10h$

$= 10 \times 25$

$= 250$.

The total wage is £250.

When $h = 40$, $W = 10 \times 40$

$= 400$.

The total wage is £400.

This is called **substituting into formulae**.

Equivalent formulae show the **same** information in different ways.

The following formulae can be used to calculate the perimeter of a rectangle:

$P = 2l + 2h$

$P = l + l + h + h$

Example – Writing formulae

Dave works for Rise and Shine Window Cleaners.
Write a formula to help Dave calculate the
cost of cleaning any number of windows.

**Rise and Shine
Window Cleaners**
£5 plus £1.50
per window

Solution

The cost is £5 plus the number of windows times £1.50.
Use w to stand for the number of windows.
Use c to stand for the total cost in pounds.

$$c = 5 + w \times 1.5 \quad \longleftarrow \quad \boxed{\text{£1.50 become 1.5}}$$
$$c = 5 + 1.5w \quad \longleftarrow \quad \boxed{\text{Remove the multiplication sign and put the number first.}}$$

Example – Using formulae

Pete uses this formula to work out the charges at
the Big Screen cinema

$$P = 8a + 6c$$

P stands for the total cost in pounds.

a stands for the number of adults in the party.

c stands for the number of children in the party.

Big Screen
Adults   £8
Children £6

Pete

Use Pete's formula to work out the cost for four adults and five children.

Solution

The number of adults is four and the number of children is five, so $a = 4$ and $c = 5$.

$$P = 8a + 6c$$
$$= 8 \times 4 + 6 \times 5$$
$$= 32 + 30$$
$$= 62$$

It costs £62 for four adults and five children.

Remember:

✦ A variable always represents a number, not a word.

✦ When you have written a formula, always check that it is correct by substituting different
numbers to see that it gives the right answer.

✦ Keep the equals signs underneath each other when setting out your working.

Skills practice A

1 Match these algebra cards.

2 more than n	**2 × n**	**2 less than n**	**n × 2**
2 plus n	**n + n**	**n added to n**	**n − 2**
2n	**n + 2**	**twice n**	**2 + n**

2 Write algebraic expressions for the following.

  a b plus 2   **b** 6 lots of b **c** b minus 2

  d 2 lots of b **e** 6 less than b **f** 7 more than b

  g b multiplied by 3   **h** b squared   **i** a lots of b.

3 Work out the value of these expressions.

  a $b + 7$ **b** $10b$ **c** $12 + b$.

    when   **i** $b = 2$ **ii** $b = 3$ **iii** $b = 4$.

4 a Find the values of $2c$, $3c$ and $5c$ when

     i $c = 2$ **ii** $c = 3$ **iii** $c = 4$.

  b For each value of c, show that $2c + 3c$ is the same as $5c$.

5 Work out the value of $3a + 2b$ when

  a $a = 2$ and $b = 3$ **b** $a = 4$ and $b = 5$

  c $a = 4$ and $b = 1$ **d** $a = 0$ and $b = 7$.

6 a A school shop sells calculators for £3 each.

     i The shop sells five calculators.
        How much money has the shop received?

     ii A formula is used to work out the takings at the end of the day.
        c stands for the number of calculators sold.
        T stands for the amount of money received in pounds.
        Which of these formulae is correct?

$T = c \div 3$	$T = c + 3$	$T = 3c$

  b The shop also sells geometry sets for £2 each.
     g stands for the number of geometry sets sold.
     Write an expression for the amount of money received for geometry sets.

  c What does the formula $T = 3c + 2g$ work out?

7 A shop sells clothes.

Jeans   £30
T-shirts   £10

a Write down how you would work out the cost of
   i two pairs of jeans and three T-shirts
   ii three pairs of jeans and four T-shirts.

b Use j for the number of pairs of jeans.
   Use t for the number of T-shirts.
   Copy and complete this formula.

   Cost (£) = 30 × ☐ + 10 ☐

c Work out the cost of four pairs of jeans and three T-shirts.

Skills practice B

1 Ella is going on holiday to Denmark.
   She buys currency from her local bank.
   She is given 8.5 Danish kroner for every pound.
   p stands for the number of pounds.
   k stands for the number of kroner.

a Two of these formulae are correct.
   Which ones are they?

   $k = p ÷ 8.5$ $k = p + 8.5$ $p = k ÷ 8.5$

   $k = 8.5p$ $p = 8.5k$

b Ella exchanges £200.
   How many kroner does she receive?

2 A bicycle shop uses this formula to calculate the cost of hiring bicycles.

   $C = 2.50h + 10$

   C stands for cost in pounds and h for the number of hours.
   Calculate the cost for

   a 3 hours   **b** 5 hours   **c** 8 hours.

Reasoning

3 a Use the formula
$C = 5b - 2$
to find the value of C when

   i $b = 2$ **iii** $b = 12$

   ii $b = 8$ **iv** $b = 20$.

b The formula refers to the notice about paperback books.

   i What does b stand for?   **ii** What does C stand for?

4 Look at this advert.

Mark writes down a formula.
$P = 12a + 10c$

a What do a and c stand for in Mark's formula?

b Work out the cost for

   i three adults and four children

   ii five adults and ten children.

5 George, Sue and Gary have answered the same question but they get different answers.

Name: George	Name: Sue	Name: Gary
Find the value of $5a + 2b$ when $a = 3$ and $b = 4$.	Find the value of $5a + 2b$ when $a = 3$ and $b = 4$.	Find the value of $5a + 2b$ when $a = 3$ and $b = 4$.
$5a + 2b$	$5a + 2b$	$5a + 2b$
$= 53 + 24$	$= 5 + 3 + 2 + 4$	$= 5 \times 3 + 2 \times 4$
$= 77$	$= 14$	$= 15 + 8$
		$= 23$

a Whose answer is correct?

b What mistakes have been made in the wrong answers?

Reasoning

Reasoning

6 You are given this formula:

$$V = 2p - 3q - r$$

Find possible values of p, q and r to give the values of V in the table.

p	q	r	Calculation	V
10	5	4	2 × 10 – 3 × 5 – 4 = 20 × 15 – 4 = 1	1
				2
				3
				10

7 Family Challenge is a TV quiz game with the following rules:
- Family teams are made up of five people and include at least two children.
- One question is put to each team member and they choose either an 'easy' or a 'hard' question.
- Each team is given £1000 playing money.
- For each correct answer the team wins £400 if the question was easy and £1000 if the question was hard.
- For each wrong answer, the team loses £200.

a Copy and complete the winnings table.

		Number of easy questions right, e					
		0	**1**	**2**	**3**	**4**	**5**
Number of hard questions right, h	0						3000
	1			2400			
	2						
	3						
	4			Winnings table (£)			
	5	6000					

b The McTaggart family got e easy questions right and h hard questions right.
Write down a formula for the number of questions that the McTaggarts got wrong.

c Find a formula for the McTaggarts' winnings.

d Check that your formula gives the numbers in your winnings table.

Wider skills practice

Reasoning

1 $y = x + 2$ is a formula that connects the x and y co-ordinates on a graph.

  a Copy and complete this table to work out the co-ordinates of some points.

x	Formula for y	Co-ordinates
0		
2		
5	$y = 5 + 2$ $= 7$	(5, 7)
8		

  b Draw a set of axes like these.
    Plot your points and join them.

  c $y = 11 - 2x$ is another formula connecting
    y and x.
    Use values of x from 0 to 4 to work out the
    values of y.

  d Plot the points on the same axes and join them.

  e The two lines cross at (3, 5).
    The values $x = 3$ and $y = 5$ fit both formulae.
    Find another formula for which $y = 5$
    when $x = 3$.

  f Plot some points using your formula from
    part **e** and join them up.
    Do the three lines all meet at (3, 5)?

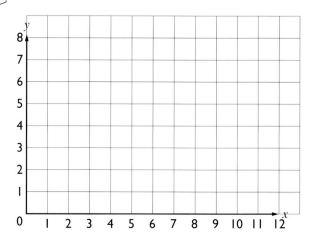

2 Pavel is investigating the angles inside isosceles triangles.

  a Copy and complete this table that he has started.

x	a	b
40°	40°	100°
50°		
60°		
70°		

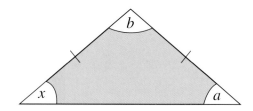

  b Fill in some other angles.
    Try as many angles as you need to find a rule for working them out quickly.

  c Pavel is making some formulae to calculate the size of the missing angles.
    He writes $a = x$ for his first formula.
    Write a formula to find b.

Reasoning

3 Tony and Charlotte are working with some sequences.
Tony uses a formula for his sequence.

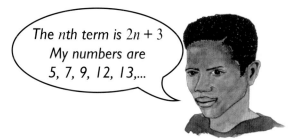

> The *n*th term is $2n + 3$
> My numbers are
> 5, 7, 9, 12, 13,...

Tony

a Tony has made a mistake with one of the numbers in his sequence.
Write down what the correct sequence should be.

b Charlotte has written her sequence in a table.
She uses *n* for the number in the sequence and *v* for the value of the term.

n	1	2	3	4	5
v	1	5	9		

She thinks that a formula for her sequence starts $v = 4n + \square$.
Copy and complete Charlotte's formula.
Substitute some values of *n* to check that it is correct.

c Tony's and Charlotte's sequences both have 9 as their third term.
Write some formulae for other sequences whose third term is 9.

Applying skills

Problem solving

a Ann has a picture that she wants to frame.
It is 50 cm high and 40 cm wide.
The picture framer in her village charges 15p per cm for
the wooden frame and 2p per cm² for the glass.

   i What is the total length of the wood used to make the frame?

   ii How much will the wood cost?

   iii What area of glass is needed?

   iv What is the cost of the glass?

b Doug wants to frame a photograph.
It is 20 cm high and 25 cm wide.
What is the cost of Doug's frame?

c Write a formula that will calculate the cost of any size of frame.
Use your answers to parts **a** and **b** to check that it is correct.

d The glass is cheaper than the wood in Doug's frame.
The wood is cheaper in Ann's.
Is there any size of frame where the wood and the glass cost the same?

Reviewing skills

1 Look at this advert.

BOAT HIRE

£4 deposit plus £5 per hour

a Copy and complete this formula.

Cost (£) = [＿＿＿＿＿＿] + [＿＿＿＿＿＿] × number of [＿＿＿＿＿＿]

b How much does it cost for
  i 1 hour   ii 2 hours   iii 3 hours?

2 Work out the value of $2a + 3b - 4c$ when
  a $a = 2$, $b = 3$ and $c = 3$
  b $a = 1$, $b = 2$ and $c = 0$
  c $a = 0$, $b = 4$ and $c = 3$
  d $a = 2$, $b = 3$ and $c = 2$.

3 Mercy is going ice-skating with her parents and three cousins. She uses this formula to work out the cost.

  Cost (£) = $5a + 3c$

  a What do a and c stand for?
  b How much does it cost for this group of people to skate?

AVONFORD
ICE RINK

Adults   £5
Children   £3

Building skills

Example outside the Maths classroom
Craft work

Toolbox

An **expression** is a collection of terms.

$4a + 6b + a - 2b + 5$

> **6b means 6 × b.**

> You usually write this as a not 1a.

> Write 4a not a4.

A **term** is a single number or a **variable**.
A term can also be a product of numbers or variables.
Here are some examples.

$$t \quad 5 \quad 3n \quad ab \quad \tfrac{1}{2}m \quad 7pq$$

Terms that contain exactly the same variable are known as **like terms**.

- 5T and 3T are like terms as they contain the same letter.
- 3a^2 and 6a^2 are also like terms.
- 6w and 3v are not like terms because they have different letters.
- 5a and 6a^2 are not like terms as they have different powers of a.

Like terms can be combined into a single term.
This is called **collecting** or **gathering** terms.

$$4a + 6b + a - 2b + 5 = 5a + 4b + 5$$

Example – Simplifying expressions involving addition and subtraction

Simplify these expressions.

a $6v - 2v + 4v$ **b** $7w + 12w^2 - 2w$

Solution

a $6v - 2v + 4v = 8v$

> The variable is the same in all three terms.

b $7w + 12w^2 - 2w = 5w + 12w^2$

> 7w and 2w are like terms.

> Make sure you keep the sign with its term.
> $7w - 2w = 5w$

> 12w^2 uses a different power of w so you cannot combine it with the other two terms.

Example – Simplifying expressions involving multiplication

Simplify this expression.

$2e \times 3f \times 4e$

Solution

$2e \times 3f \times 4e = 2 \times 3 \times 4 \times e \times f \times e$ ← **When multiplying terms, multiply the numbers together and multiply the variables together separately.**

$= 24e^2f$ ← **$e \times e = e^2$ and $e^2 \times f = e^2f$ and $24 \times e^2f = 24e^2f$**

Remember:

✦ When multiplying terms together, multiply the numbers and the variables separately.
✦ Write the numbers before the variables in a product and write the variables in alphabetical order.
✦ Multiplying by $\frac{1}{2}$ is the same as dividing by 2.
✦ h^2 means multiply h by h. It does not mean work out $h \times 2$.

Skills practice A

1 Look at these algebra walls.

a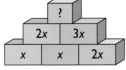

b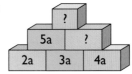

The expression in each brick is the sum of the expressions in the two bricks underneath it.
Copy the walls and find the missing expressions.

2 Simplify these expressions.

    a $m + m + m$ **b** $2h + 5h - 3h$ **c** $a + a + a + a + a$
    d $x + 2x + 3x + 4x$ **e** $3g - 2g + 4g - 2g$ **f** $5j - 2j - j + 3j$

3 Simplify these expressions.

    a $4g + 2 - 3g + 5$ **b** $2d + 4 + 5d + 7 + 3d$ **c** $4m - 2 + 4m - 3$
    d $2x + 3 - x + 2 + 4x$ **e** $3c + 2 - 2c - 1$ **f** $3y + 5 - y + 3 + 2y - 8$

4 Simplify these expressions.

    a $2c + 5d + 2c + d$ **b** $a + 2b + 4b + 3a + 3b$ **c** $3x + 2y - 3x + 4y$
    d $2g + 3f - g + 5f - g$ **e** $3m + 2n + 4n$ **f** $6p - 2q + 3 + 3p + 5q + 2$

5 Write these expressions as neatly as possible.

    a $3 \times f$ **b** $n \times n$ **c** $p \times r$
    d $a \times 2 \times c$ **e** $d \times 3 \times e$ **f** $x \times 3 \times x$

6 Which of these expressions does not simplify to $10rv$?

a $5r \times 5v$ **b** $2r \times 5v$ **c** $r \times 10v$

7 Simplify these expressions.

a $\dfrac{a}{5} + \dfrac{3a}{5}$ **b** $\dfrac{3b}{4} + \dfrac{b}{4}$ **c** $\dfrac{6c}{5} + \dfrac{2c}{5}$

d $\dfrac{3d}{5} - \dfrac{d}{5}$ **e** $\dfrac{5e}{8} - \dfrac{3e}{8}$ **f** $\dfrac{2f}{3} \times g$

Skills practice B

1 In each of these questions, you should copy the expression and then simplify it by collecting like terms.
Here is an example.

$$2a + 3b + a + 4b = 2a + a + 3b + 4b$$
$$= 3a + 7b$$

a $a + 2b + 4 + 5a$ **b** $4x + 5y - 2x + y$ **c** $2x - 3y + 6y + 7$
d $9x + 6y - 5x - 4$ **e** $3p - 4q + 7 - 3p$ **f** $4p - 5 + 3q - 4$
g $9r - 3s - 8r + 3s$ **h** $7h - 2i - 4h + 6i$ **i** $5x + 2y + 3x - 6y - 8x$

2 Sam, Rob and Sean were adding up the number of goals they had scored in football that season.
Sam scored x goals.
Rob scored three more than Sam.
Sean scored twice the number that Sam did.
Write down and simplify an expression for the total number of goals scored by all three boys.

3 Look at these triangles.

A   **B** 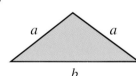   **C**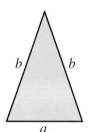

a Match the triangles with these formulae for their perimeters.
Perimeter $= a + b + b$
Perimeter $= 2a + b$
Perimeter $= a + a + b$
Perimeter $= 3a$
Perimeter $= a + a + a$
Perimeter $= a + 2b$

b Work out the perimeter of each triangle when
  i $a = 4$ and $b = 2$
  ii $a = 5$ and $b = 3$
c Is $3a$ always the same as $a + a + a$?
d Is $2a + b$ always the same as $a + a + b$?

4 Simplify these expressions.

a $b \times b$ b $3c \times c$ c $z \times 2z$

d $3g \times 2g$ e $a \times b$ f $a \times a \times a$

g $3f \times g$ h $c \times 3d$ i $2x \times 3y$

j $4s \times 5t$ k $2a \times 3b \times 4a$ l $2a^2 + 3a^2 + 4a^2 + 5a^2$

m $4m^2 - 2m^2 + 3m^2 - m^2$ n $3c^2 + 2c^2 + c^2 + 4d^2 + 5d^2$

Wider skills practice

1 Look at these three diagrams of a kite.

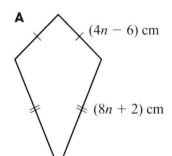

A $(4n - 6)$ cm $(8n + 2)$ cm

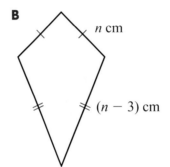

B n cm $(n - 3)$ cm

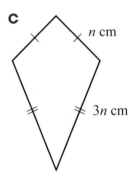

C n cm $3n$ cm

a In which kite are the longer sides 3 cm more than the shorter sides?

b Find and simplify an expression for the perimeter of each kite.

c What is the perimeter of each kite when $n = 5$?

d Draw and label a different shape whose perimeter is the same as the expression that you found in part **b** for kite A.

2 a i Write down an expression for the sum of the angles in this triangle.

   ii Simplify your expression.

b What do the angles in a triangle add up to?

c What is the value of x?

d Write down the size of each of the three angles.

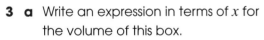

$4x$

$2x$

$3x$

3 a Write an expression in terms of x for the volume of this box.

b Find the volume of the box when $x = 2$.

c The box has a top and a bottom. Write down and simplify an expression for the total surface area of the box in terms of x.

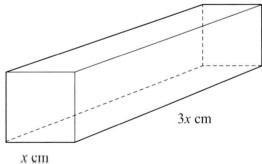

x cm x cm $3x$ cm

Reasoning

4 Look at this cuboid made out of straws.

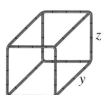

a Write down and simplify an expression for the total length of straw.

b The total length of straw needed is 48 cm.

   i What are the possible whole number values of x, y and z?

   ii Which set of values gives the greatest volume?

Applying skills

1 In the Fibonacci sequence, each term is the sum of the previous two.

    1, 1, 2, 3, 5, 8, ...

A Fibonacci sequence can start with any two numbers.

    4, 2, 6, 8, 14, 22, 36, 58, 94, 152

Sally is trying out a trick on a friend.

She asks her friend to write any two numbers in the first boxes of a 2 by 5 grid.

4	2			

Sally then puts on a blindfold.

She asks her friend to fill the rest of the grid with Fibonacci sequence numbers, using a calculator if needed.

4	2	6	8	14
22	36	58	94	152

Sally then removes her blindfold, has a quick glance at the grid and writes a number on a piece of paper.

396

She asks her friend to add up all the numbers in the grid and the answer is exactly the same as the number that Sally wrote down so quickly.

$4 + 2 + 6 + 8 + 14 + 22 + 36 + 58 + 94 + 152 = 396$

How does the trick work?

Use these steps to help you.

a Use a and b to stand for the first two numbers.
The next number is equal to $a + b$.
Write expressions for each of the other Fibonacci numbers and write them in a grid.

b Find an expression for the grid total.

c Look for a connection between the total and one of the other boxes in the grid.

d Can you explain how the trick works now?

e Practise the simple mental calculation that is needed and then try out the trick on some friends.

2 Look at this square.

$x - 3$	$x + 2$	$x + 1$
$x + 4$	x	$x - 4$
$x - 1$	$x - 2$	$x + 3$

a Copy the square substituting the value $x = 5$.

b What do you notice about the sum of all the rows, columns and diagonals?

c Copy it again but this time substituting $x = 8$.

d What do you notice this time?

e What is the connection between parts **b** and **d** and the value of x each time?

f Prove that this will always be the case.

g Copy and complete this magic square.

$x - 4$	$x + 1$	
	$x - 1$	

Reviewing skills

1 Simplify these expressions.

　a $6d + 7d - 5d$

　b $8m - 10m$

　c $g^2 + 3g^2$

　d $5r + 11r^2 - 2r$

2 a Which of these expressions is largest when $a = 6$?

A $\dfrac{3a - 4}{2}$　　B $a^2 - 2$　　C $\dfrac{1}{2}(a + 2)$

　b Find a value of a for which a^2 2 has the smallest value of the three expressions.

　c Find a value of a for which two of the expressions are equal.

3 The expression in each brick of this algebra wall is the sum of the expressions in the two bricks underneath it.
Copy the wall and find the missing expressions in i and ii.

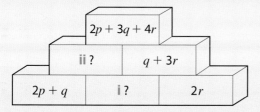

Building skills

Example outside the Maths classroom

Building regulations

Toolbox

Number machines can help you work with formulae.

The cost, C pence, of a bus ticket for a journey of m miles is given by the formula
$$C = 20m + 50.$$
You can write this using a number machine.

$$m \longrightarrow \boxed{\times 20} \xrightarrow{20m} \boxed{+ 50} \longrightarrow 20m + 50 = C$$

For a journey of 7 miles, $m = 7$.

$$7 \longrightarrow \boxed{\times 20} \xrightarrow{140} \boxed{+ 50} \longrightarrow 190$$

The cost is 190 pence or £1.90.

You can use a number machine in reverse.

This well tell you the number of miles you can travel for a certain amount of money.

Work from right to left with the **inverse operations**.

So, for a fare of £1.30, the number machine looks like this.

$$4 \longleftarrow \boxed{\div 20} \xleftarrow{80} \boxed{- 50} \longleftarrow 130$$

You can travel 4 miles.

Example – Changing a formula

The Williams family are going on holiday to Florida.

a The exchange rate is 1.6 dollars to the pound.
Write a formula to represent this information.

b They wish to take $1200 with them.
How many pounds should they change into dollars?

Solution

a Number of dollars = number of pounds × 1.6
If D is the number of dollars and P is the number of pounds then $D = 1.6P$

b The formula is used in reverse to find the
number of pounds.

Number of pounds = number of dollars ÷ 1.6

$\qquad\qquad\qquad\quad = 1200 \div 1.6$

$\qquad\qquad\qquad\quad = 750$

> To find the number of dollars you multiplied by 1.6, so to find the number of pounds you must divide by 1.6.

They need to change £750 into dollars.

Example – Substituting values into a formula

This formula gives p in terms of e and g.

$$p = \frac{3e - g}{4}$$

Find the values of p when

a $e = 4$ and $g = 0$ **b** $e = 5$ and $g = 7$ **c** $e = 8$ and $g = 20$

d $e = 4$ and $g = 12$ **e** $e = 100$ and $g = 296$

Solution

a $\dfrac{3e - g}{4} = \dfrac{3 \times 4 - 0}{4}$ > Substitute the values given for the variables.

$\qquad = \dfrac{12 - 0}{4} = \dfrac{12}{4} = 3$ > Calculate the numerator first.

b $\dfrac{3e - g}{4} = \dfrac{3 \times 5 - 7}{4}$ **c** $\dfrac{3e - g}{4} = \dfrac{3 \times 8 - 20}{4}$

$\qquad = \dfrac{15 - 7}{4} = \dfrac{8}{4} = 2$ $= \dfrac{24 - 20}{4} = \dfrac{4}{4} = 1$

d $\dfrac{3e - g}{4} = \dfrac{3 \times 4 - 12}{4}$ **e** $\dfrac{3e - g}{4} = \dfrac{3 \times 100 - 296}{4}$

$\qquad = \dfrac{12 - 12}{4} = \dfrac{0}{4} = 0$ $= \dfrac{300 - 296}{4} = \dfrac{4}{4} = 1$

Example – Using number machines

A train company uses a formula to work out the time, t minutes, for a rail journey from London to Plymouth.

The number of stops along the way is s.

$$t = 5s + 165$$

a Use a number machine to find the time for a journey with seven stops.

b A train takes 3 hours and 10 minutes to travel from Plymouth to London.
How many stops did it make?

Solution

a Here is the number machine for this formula.

$$s \longrightarrow \boxed{\times 5} \xrightarrow{5s} \boxed{+ 165} \longrightarrow 5s + 165 = t$$

When there are seven stops,

$$7 \longrightarrow \boxed{\times 5} \xrightarrow{35} \boxed{+ 165} \longrightarrow 200$$

It takes 200 minutes or 3 hours and 20 minutes.

b For a journey of 190 minutes, reverse the number machine. ⟵ Convert 3 hours and 10 minutes into minutes.

$$5 \longleftarrow \boxed{\div 5} \xleftarrow{25} \boxed{- 165} \longleftarrow 190$$

The train made five stops.

> **Remember:**
>
> ✦ A variable must always stand for a number. It is not an abbreviation for a word.
> ✦ To reverse a number machine, replace each operation with its inverse and work from right to left.

Skills practice A

1 The opposite of 'turn left' is 'turn right'.
Write down the opposites of these instructions.

   a Turn right.

   b Pump up a tyre.

   c Stand up.

   d Walk five steps backwards.

   e Turn 45° clockwise.

   f Climb 10 steps up a ladder.

2 Find the output for each of these number machines.

a 32 ⟶ − 17 ⟶ ☐   **b** 27 ⟶ + 8 ⟶ ☐

c 40 ⟶ ÷ 5 ⟶ ☐   **d** 5 ⟶ × 3 ⟶ ☐

3 Work out the rules for these adding and subtracting number machines.
Write down your rule in words.

a 7 ⟶ ☐ ⟶ 10   **b** 12 ⟶ ☐ ⟶ 8

c 8 ⟶ ☐ ⟶ 1   **d** 3 ⟶ ☐ ⟶ 13

4 The number machines in question **3** can also work backwards.
Write down the new rule for each one in words.

a 7 ⟵ ☐ ⟵ 10   **b** 12 ⟵ ☐ ⟵ 8

c 8 ⟵ ☐ ⟵ 1   **d** 3 ⟵ ☐ ⟵ 13

5 Here are six instructions.
Two of them are inverse instructions of each other.

Add 5	Multiply by 3	Multiply by 10
Subtract 10	Divide by 3	Add 3

a Write down the pair of inverse instructions.

b Write the inverse instruction for each of the four that are left.

6 Tim buys some CDs.

Mega Sale

All CDs only £12 each

a Copy and complete this number machine.
It works out how much Tim spends.

Number of CDs ⟶ ? ⟶ Cost (£)

b Tim buys four CDs.
Use the number machine to find out how much he spends.

c Arran buys some CDs in the same sale.
He spends £72.
Use a number machine to find out how many CDs he buys.

7 Jarrad has a pay-as-you-go phone tariff.

All calls cost 10p per minute.

He tops up with £20.

a How much does he pay for a 6-minute call?

b Copy and complete this number machine to work out how much Jarrad pays for his calls.

c Jarrad has £4.60 credit left. Reverse your number machine to work out how many minutes of calls he can make.

8 Pete is building a fence.

He uses these formulae.

Number of posts = number of sections + 1

Number of bars = 3 × number of sections

a Work out how many posts Pete needs for

   i two sections   **ii** three sections

   iii four sections   **iv** five sections.

This is one section of Pete's fence.

b Work out how many bars Pete needs for

   i two sections   **ii** three sections

   iii four sections   **iv** five sections.

c How many sections does Pete build when he uses

   i 7 posts   **iii** 10 posts

   ii 8 posts   **iv** 20 posts?

d How many sections does Pete build when he uses

   i 18 bars   **ii** 21 bars

   iii 30 bars   **iv** 42 bars?

Skills practice B

1 This formula gives the cost C, in pence, of buying n packets of crisps at a shop.

$C = 20n$

Mercy buys some crisps.

Use a number machine to work out how many packets of crisps she buys when she spends

a 40p   **b** 60p   **c** £1   **d** £1.60.

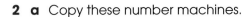

2 a Copy these number machines.

i $v \longrightarrow$ ☐ × 2 $\longrightarrow$ ☐ + 5 $\longrightarrow w$ **ii** $v \longrightarrow$ ☐ × 5 $\longrightarrow$ ☐ + 2 $\longrightarrow w$

iii $v \longrightarrow$ ☐ + 2 $\longrightarrow$ ☐ × 5 $\longrightarrow w$ **iv** $v \longrightarrow$ ☐ ÷ 2 $\longrightarrow$ ☐ + 5 $\longrightarrow w$

Some of these formulae match the number machines.
Label your diagrams with any that match.

$w = \frac{1}{2}v + 5$ $w = 5v + 2$

b Draw the inverse of each number machine.

3 Michelle wants to use this number machine.
One of the instructions is missing.

$4 \longrightarrow$ ☐ × 5 $\longrightarrow$ ☐ $\longrightarrow 21$

a Find the missing instruction.

b Michelle now uses some different inputs.
She makes a table of her results.
Are they correct?

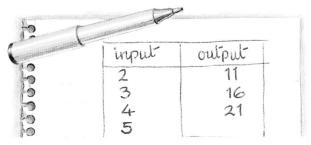

input	output
2	11
3	16
4	21
5	

c What is the output for these inputs?
   i 1   **ii** 5   **iii** 7   **iv** 20

d Find the inputs for these outputs.
   i 41   **ii** 51   **iii** 76   **iv** 126

4 Ali writes down a formula to work out the cost of a meal for her family.

Cost = 12p + 5

a What does p stand for?

b How much is a meal for six people?

c The bill is £53.
How many people are there in Ali's family?

> *Any
> 3-course meal*
> **£12 per person**
> *plus*
> *£5 service charge per table*

Reasoning

Reasoning

5 a Speedy Motors is a car rental firm.
They charge £25 per day.

    i Write a formula connecting d, the number of days, with C, the cost in pounds.

    ii What is the cost of a six-day hire?

    iii Dave pays £250 to hire a car. How many days does the rental last?

b Rent the Best is another car hire firm.
They charge £40 flat rate plus £10 per day.

Pete paid £250 to hire a car from Rent The Best.
How many days was this for?

c i Sarah wants to hire a car but doesn't know whether to use Speedy Motors or Rent the Best.
What advice would you give her?

    ii Sarah paid £280 for her car rental.
Which company did she use?
Explain your answer.

Wider skills practice

1 To change metres to centimetres Ken multiplies by 100.

    a Draw a number machine to show this.

    b How does Ken change centimetres into metres?

2 This is the formula for the area of a rectangle.

    area = length × width

Find the missing length for each of these rectangles.

a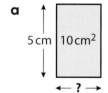
5 cm | 10 cm² | ← ? →

b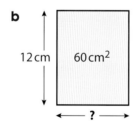
12 cm | 60 cm² | ? →

c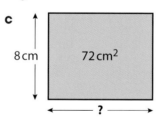
8 cm | 72 cm² | ← ? →

3 a Write down the formula for the area of this parallelogram.

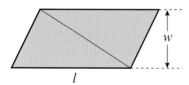

    b The parallelogram is divided in half along the red line.
Use your formula for the area of a parallelogram to find a formula for the area of a triangle.

    c The area of a triangle is 24 cm² and it has a base of 16 cm.

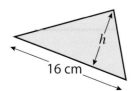

    What is the height, h, of the triangle?

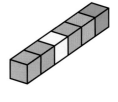

4 This stick is made out of six cubes.
It is lying on a table.

   a How many of the cubes' faces is it possible to see?

   b How many of the cubes' faces are hidden?

   c Find a formula to calculate the number of faces showing in a stick n cubes long.

   d Find a formula to calculate the number of hidden faces in a stick n cubes long.

5 a Draw a pair of axes taking x and y from 0 to 8.
   Plot the points A(1, 6), B(2, 3) and C(0, 4) and join them to form triangle ABC.

   b A translation maps every point (x, y) to a new point $(x + 5, y - 3)$.

   The new points are A', B' and C'.

   Draw the triangle A' B' C' on your diagram.

   c Copy these number machines.

   Complete them to show how the new co-ordinates are calculated.

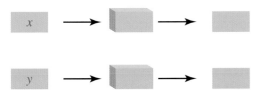

   d Work out the inverse number machines for x and y.

   e Draw another shape on your diagram and translate it using the inverse machines from part **d**.
   What do you notice?

6 This diagram shows a network with nodes, arcs and regions.
   The numbers of each are N, A and R.

   a Draw networks for which

   i $N = 2, A = 2$ and $R = 2$

   ii $N = 3, A = 3$ and $R = 2$

   iii $N = 4, A = 5$ and $R = 3$.

   b Samir has worked out a rule.

The rule is $N = A - R + 2$.

Samir

   i Use Samir's rule to find R when $N = 5$ and $A = 7$.

   ii Draw a network with these values of N, A and R.

arc

node

region

The outside is also a region.

Reasoning

Applying skills

1 Aisha's thermometer only has a centigrade scale.
Her American friend wants to know the temperature in Fahrenheit.

Aisha's Gran tells her to
multiply the centigrade temperature by 9, then divide by 5 and add 32.

a Draw a three-stage number machine to show this.

b The temperature is 20 °C.
Convert this to Fahrenheit.

c Aisha's friend has been on holiday to Dubai.
The temperature reached 113 °F. What is this in centigrade?

d Find a temperature which has the same value when measured in °F and °C.

2 The pentagon shown has been split into triangles by drawing diagonals from one corner. In this case there are five outside edges and three triangles.

Experiment with other polygons and find a formula that connects the number of outside edges, n, with the number of triangles, t.

a Write the formula with t as the subject.

b Write the formula with n as the subject.

c How many triangles do you get from a ten-sided polygon (a decagon)?

d How many sides does a polygon have if it can be split into ten triangles?

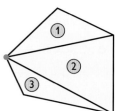

Reviewing skills

1 Ken is changing a distance from miles to kilometres.
He divides the number of miles by 5 and then multiplies by 8.

a Draw a number machine to show this.

b Use your number machine to convert 75 miles into kilometres.

c Draw the inverse number machine.

d Ken drives 120 km.
Use your inverse machine to find out how many miles this is.

2 Two plumbers are advertising their services.

> ## JIM THE PIPE
> **£20 per hour**
> **plus**
> **£40 call-out charge**

> ## WATER WIZARD
> Only £16 per hour
> Plus £60
> call-out charge

a Draw a number machine to show how to work out the cost of a visit from each plumber.

b Omar has a burst pipe.
It will take 2 hours to repair.
Which plumber should he use?

c Tim needs a plumber for a five-minute job.
Which plumber should he use?

d Serena's bill from Jim the Pipe is £140.

   i How long did the job take?

   ii How much would the Water Wizard have charged?

Unit 5 · Setting up and solving simple equations · Band f

Building skills

Example outside the Maths classroom

Fencing enclosures

Toolbox

An **equation** says that one expression is equal to another.
For example:

$$4x - 3 = 17$$

Solving an equation means finding the value of x that makes the equation true.

You can solve an equation using the balance method.
You must keep the equation balanced, like a pair of weighing scales, by doing the *same* operation to *both* sides.

$$4x - 3 = 17$$
$$+3 \qquad 4x = 20 \qquad +3$$
$$\div 4 \qquad x = 5 \qquad \div 4$$

> The inverse of subtract 3 is add 3.
> Make sure you add 3 to *both* sides.

> The inverse of multiply by 4 is divide by 4.

$x = 5$ is the solution.

Example – Solving 'think of a number' problems

Sophie thinks of a number.

Solution

You can write an equation and solve it to find Sophie's number.
Let n represent her number.

$$n \times 9 - 11 = 52$$
$$9n - 11 = 52$$

Using the balance method rewrite this using correct algebraic notation.

> *When I multiply my number by 9 and subtract 11, the answer is 52. What is my number?*

Sophie

$$9n - 11 = 52$$
$$+11 \qquad 9n = 63 \qquad +11$$
$$\div 9 \qquad n = 7 \qquad \div 9$$

> The inverse of subtract 11 is add 11.

> Add 11 to both sides.

> The inverse of multiply by 9 is divide by 9.

Check: $9 \times 7 - 11 = 63 - 11 = 52$ ✓

> Always check your work.

Example – Solving word problems

Three friends run a relay race.
Altogether their time is 65 seconds.
Harry takes 4 seconds longer than Dan.
Millie takes 5 seconds less than Dan.
How many seconds does each person take?

Solution

First write the expressions for the time each person takes.
Let s stand for the number of seconds that Dan takes.

Dan: s seconds
Harry: $s + 4$ seconds
Millie: $s - 5$ seconds
Total: 65 seconds

So,

$$s + s + 4 + s - 5 = 65$$ ← The total of the three expressions is 65.

$$3s - 1 = 65$$ ← Collect like terms.

$$3s = 66$$ ← Add 1 to both sides.

$$s = 22$$ ← Divide both sides by 3

So Dan takes 22 seconds.

Harry takes 26 seconds. ← Harry's time is $s + 4 = 22 + 4 = 26$ seconds.

Millie takes 17 seconds. ← Millie's time is $s - 5 = 22 - 5 = 17$ seconds.

Check: 22 + 26 + 17 = 65 ✓

Remember:

+ Always substitute your solution back into the equation to check it is right.
+ Make sure the equation balances at every step.
+ 'Undo' addition and subtraction first.
+ Then undo multiplication and division.
+ Whatever you do, do it to both sides.

Skills practice A

1 Write equations for each of the following sets of scales. Solve your equations. Draw the scales at each stage in your working.

a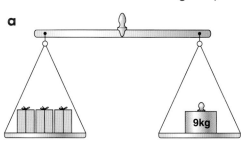

b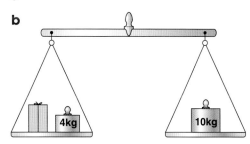

c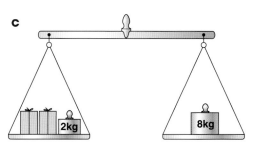

d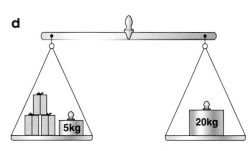

e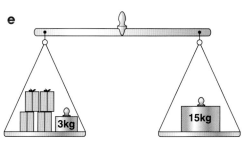

f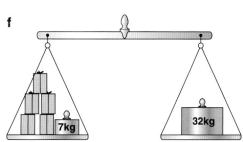

2 Solve these equations by subtracting from both sides.

    a $m + 4 = 11$ **b** $a + 11 = 15$ **c** $6 + b = 8$

    d $x + 5 = 15$ **e** $y + 7 = 17$ **f** $z + 15 = 115$

3 Solve these equations by adding to both sides.

    a $p - 6 = 10$ **b** $d - 7 = 13$ **c** $a - 4 = 4$

    d $q - 5 = 15$ **e** $s - 9 = 15$ **f** $t - 25 = 975$

4 Solve these equations.
(You will need to decide whether to add or subtract in each case.)

    a $c - 7 = 10$ **b** $5 + d = 7$ **c** $g - 5 = 5$

    d $u + 5 = 19$ **e** $h - 8 = 42$ **f** $j + 125 = 1125$

5 Solve these equations.

    a $p + 7 = 13$ **b** $10 + f = 14$ **c** $h - 5 = 6$

    d $b + 3 = 8$ **e** $g - 8 = 12$ **f** $12 + k = 13$

6 Solve these equations by dividing both sides of the equations by the same amount.

    a $2a = 6$ **b** $4b = 12$ **c** $3m = 15$

    d $4a = 16$ **e** $3s = 18$ **f** $5r = 20$

    g $7n = 42$ **h** $10x = 70$ **i** $12y = 132$

7 Solve these equations by multiplying both sides of the equation by the same amount.

a $\dfrac{c}{3} = 5$ **b** $\dfrac{d}{2} = 3$ **c** $\dfrac{g}{5} = 5$

d $\dfrac{t}{9} = 4$ **e** $\dfrac{x}{2} = 5$ **f** $\dfrac{r}{4} = 10$

8 Jo has a pencils and Humza has b pencils.

Write in words the meaning of each of these equations.

a $a = 8$ **b** $a + b = 12$ **c** $a = 2b$

9 Solve these equations.

a $5p = 20$ **b** $6 + f = 7$ **c** $8a = 32$

d $g - 2 = 8$ **e** $m - 11 = 21$ **f** $9h = 36$

g $12x = 72$ **h** $y - 8 = 22$ **i** $\dfrac{y}{7} = 1$

10 Here is Jamie's maths homework.

1. $5x - 3 = 7$ $5x - 3 + 3 = 7 + 3$ $5x = 10$ $5x \div 5 = 10 \div 5$ $x = 2$	**2.** $2x - 4 = 14$ $2x - 4 + 4 = 14 - 4$ $2x = 10$ $2x \div 2 = 10 \div 2$ $x = 5$
3. $3x - 1 = 26$ $3x - 1 + 1 = 26 + 1$ $3x = 27$ $3x \div 3 = 27 \div 3$ $x = 9$	**4.** $4x + 3 = 24$ $4x \div 4 + 3 = 24 \div 4$ $x + 3 - 3 = 6 - 3$ $x = 3$

a Check Jamie's homework.

b Jamie got some of the questions wrong.
State the correct answers.

11 Meena and Alan are having an argument.

The answer to $5x - 12 = 18$ is $x = 5$.

No, it isn't. It is $x = 3$.

Meena   Alan

a Who is right?

b How can you tell an answer is wrong?

c What is the right answer?

12 Solve these equations.

  a $2a + 3 = 5$ **b** $4d + 1 = 9$ **c** $2 + 2c = 8$

  d $6c + 2 = 20$ **e** $6m + 4 = 16$ **f** $3d + 2 = 5$

  g $12x + 6 = 30$ **h** $5y - 18 = 22$ **i** $999z + 999 = 999$

13 Solve these equations.

  a $5x + 6 = 16$ **b** $3a - 7 = 14$ **c** $10 + 3f = 19$

  d $12 + 7g = 33$ **e** $5p - 12 = 8$ **f** $11j - 11 = 22$

Skills practice B

1 Solve these equations.

  a $3a + 4 = 10$ **b** $5d + 3 = 18$ **c** $2s - 6 = 4$

  d $2n - 4 = 8$ **e** $6b + 5 = 17$ **f** $4c - 5 = 11$

  g $2x + 5 = 45$ **h** $3y - 8 = 28$ **i** $9z + 35 = 125$

  j $a + 5 = 5$ **k** $2b - 7 = 7$ **l** $100c + 500 = 1500$

  m $4n + 7 = 15$ **n** $3t - 12 = 3$ **o** $4 + 3d = 19$

  p $7q - 24 = 4$ **q** $2f - 7 = 3$ **r** $4k + 8 = 24$

  s $6h - 5 = 1$ **t** $18 + 6r = 30$

2 a Match each of these equations with its solution.

  i $3x - 2 = 10$

  ii $5x - 1 = 24$

  iii $4x + 11 = 17$

  iv $2x + 5 = 10$

  v $3x - 33 = 0$

$x = 5$	$x = 2\frac{1}{2}$	$x = 1\frac{1}{2}$	$x = 3$	$x = 2$	$x = 11$	$x = 4$

  b Which two values of x are not used?
   Write your own equations with these values of x as their solutions.

3 Solve each of these equations.
 Make sure that each side of the equation balances the other.
 Check each of your solutions.

  a $\dfrac{x}{3} = 20$ **b** $\dfrac{x}{2} = \dfrac{5}{2}$ **c** $\dfrac{1}{2}x = 5$

  d $\dfrac{3}{4}x = 100$ **e** $\dfrac{2x}{3} = 8$ **f** $\dfrac{x}{6} + 3 = 9$

  g $\dfrac{x}{8} - 2 = 0$ **h** $7 - \dfrac{x}{4} = 4$

Reasoning

Reasoning

4 Leah and Ryan are making up equations for each other to solve.

Solve $5x + 2 = 17$

Leah

Solve $3x = 9$

Ryan

a What is the value of x in each case?

b Write down five other equations which have the same solution.

5 Tim is buying some fish and chips in Calais.
He pays €13 for three portions of fish and four portions of chips.

a Write down an equation to show this information.
Use f to represent the cost of one portion of fish.

b Solve your equation to work out the price of one portion of fish.

c Check your answer.

Fish & Chips

Chips €1   Fish €

6 One cinema ticket costs £c.
Pat buys five tickets.
She gets £10 change from £60.
Write an equation for c and solve it.
Check your answer.

7 Jenny thinks of a number.

I multiply my number by 4 and add 6. My answer is 30.

Jenny

a Write down an equation for Jenny's number.

b Solve your equation to work out Jenny's number.

8 Callum thinks of a number.

I multiply my number by 2 and subtract 4. My answer is 8.

Callum

a Write down an equation for Callum's number.

b Solve your equation to work out Callum's number.

9 Steve buys five pens in a shop for £1.20.

    a Write an equation for this information using p pence as the cost of one pen.

    b Solve your equation to find the cost of one pen.

10 Kate buys two apples, at 24p each, and four bananas.

    She spends £1.28 altogether.

    a Write an equation for this information, using b pence as the cost of one banana.

    b Solve your equation to find the cost of one banana.

11 Solve each of these equations.

    Make sure that each side of the equation balances the other.

    Check each of your solutions.

    a $2r = 4.2$ **b** $s + 6.2 = 11$ **c** $5.4 = 8 - t$

    d $4u - 5.6 = 10$ **e** $9.5 = 7.1 + 3y$

12 Solve these equations.

    a $-4j = 12$ **b** $10 - 2k = 8$ **c** $7 - 4l = 15$

    d $6 - 2m = 0$ **e** $15 - 3n = 1.2$ **f** $3 = 4 - \dfrac{p}{4}$

13 April is six years older than her brother Daniel.

    In 16 years the sum of their ages will be 100 years. Suppose that April is x years old now.

    a Copy and complete the table.

	April's age (years)	Daniel's age (years)
Now	x	$x - 6$
In 16 years		

    b Form an equation and solve it.

    c State their present ages.

14 Peter is four times as old as his daughter Tara.

    In five years' time their ages will total 50 years.

    a Copy and complete this table.

	Peter's age (years)	Tara's age (years)
Now	$4x$	x
In 5 years		

    b Form an equation and solve it.

    c State Peter's and Tara's present ages.

Reasoning

Reasoning

Reasoning

15 Three prizes are given from a prize fund, with these conditions.

* The first prize is twice the third prize.
* The second prize is £5 more than the third prize.

a Find the values of the prizes when the total prize money is

 i £65

 ii £37.

b It is decided that the first prize must be at least £5 more than the second prize. Investigate the total prize money needed to meet all three conditions.

Wider skills practice

1 Mike has a set of four steps.
The tread is twice the riser.
Mike has a 108 cm length of carpet that covers the steps exactly.

a Write an equation to show this information.

b Solve the equation to find

 i the height of the riser

 ii the width of the tread.

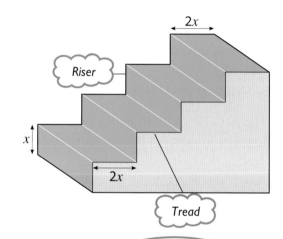

Riser

Tread

2 For each of these triangles

a write an equation for the sum of the angles in the triangle

b solve your equation

c find the size of each angle in the triangle.

Hint: Remember that the angles in a triangle add up to 180°.

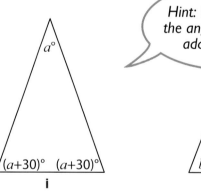

i

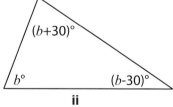

ii

3 Both these rectangles have a perimeter of 30 cm.

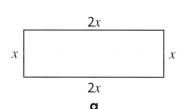

a

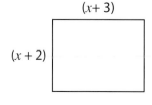

b

Find the length and width of each rectangle.

4 Each obtuse angle of a parallelogram is 32° more than each acute angle.
Let one obtuse angle be x.
Form an equation for x and solve it.
Find all the angles of the parallelogram.

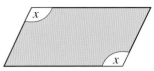

5 Each of the equal angles of an isosceles triangle is 24° greater than the third angle.
Form a suitable equation and find all three angles.

6 Sunita has 60 metres of wire netting.

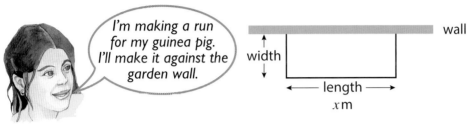

I'm making a run for my guinea pig. I'll make it against the garden wall.

wall

width

length
x m

Sunita

a She makes the run 10 metres wide.
The length of the run is x m.
Form an equation for x and solve it.

b What is the area of the run?

c Sunita wants to make the area of the run as big as possible.
She tries some different widths.
Copy and complete this table.

Width (m)	Length (m)	Area (m²)
10		
8		
6		
4		
12		
15		

d What width gives the largest area?

7 This swimming pool is a rectangle l metres long and w metres wide.

a Write down an expression for the perimeter of the pool.

b The perimeter is 26 m.
Find possible whole number values for l and w.

c Write an expression for the area of the surface of the pool in terms of l and w.

d Find the area of the surface when

  i $l = 11$ and $w = 2$

  ii $l = 9$ and $w = 4$

  iii $l = 7$ and $w = 6$.

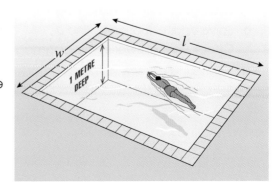

1 METRE DEEP

43

8 The picture shows a model of a garden swing seat.
The frame is made out of thin wire.
The lengths are in centimetres.
Each end is in the shape of a right-angled triangle.

a Write down a formula for the perimeter of each triangle.

b Write down a formula for the total length of wire.
Simplify your expression.

c The back, sides and seat are made out of cardboard.
Write a formula for the area of cardboard.

> **Remember: The area of a
> triangle is $\frac{1}{2}$ × base × height.**

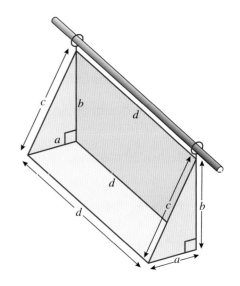

Applying skills

1 Tom and his mother have the same birthday.
When Tom is 12, his mother is 48.
Find the answer to his mother's question.

*Mum, you are
four times as old
as me.*

*How old will we
be when my age is
three times yours?*

2 a Copy this arithmagon.
The number in the square is the sum of those
in the two circles on either side.
Fill in the bottom circles in terms of a.

b Use your answers to part **a** to write an equation
in terms of a and the number 28.

c Solve your equation to find a.
Check your answer in the arithmagon.

d Copy and complete this arithmagon.

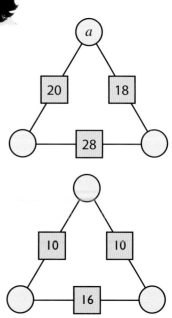

Problem solving

3 Three friends play a computer game.
Between them they score 530 points.
Rob scores 30 points more than Beth.
Millie scores twice as many points as Rob.
How many points does each friend score?

4 This tent frame is made from aluminium tubing.
The measurements are in metres.
The length x is called the 'size' of the tent.

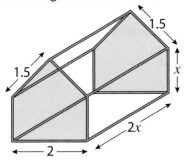

a Write down the formula for the total length of tubing needed.
b i The size of a tent is 1.8 m.
How much tubing is needed?
ii A tent uses 25 m of tubing.
What is its size?
iii A tent uses 30 m of tubing.
What is its size?

5 Solve these puzzles by finding the value of each shape.

i

☺	✋	☺	21
⌘	✋	☺	19
⌘	✋	⌘	17
14	27	16	

In these puzzles, the numbers are the row and column totals.

ii

☆	⧗	🔔	20
⧗	☆	✿	
✿	✿	✿	12
🔔	⧗	🔔	22
	25	22	

6 The length of a rectangle is 4 times its width.
The perimeter is 50 cm.
Find the area of the rectangle.

⬇ Reviewing skills

1 Solve these equations.

   a $a + 3 = 8$ **b** $b - 7 = 1$ **c** $1 + c = 14$

   d $\dfrac{d}{12} = 2$ **e** $2e = 10$ **f** $7 + f = 18$

   g $4g = 32$ **h** $\dfrac{h}{9} = 1$ **i** $4 + i = 17$

2 Solve these equations.

   a $2a + 1 = 5$ **b** $3b + 6 = 27$ **c** $5c - 4 = 16$

   d $3 + 7d = 10$ **e** $10g - 22 = 38$ **f** $3h - 6 = 0$

3 Solve these equations.

   a $3x - 4 = 5$ **b** $5x - 7 = 13$ **c** $4t + 3 = 15$

   d $9x + 3 = 30$ **e** $8p - 5 = 59$ **f** $6x + 8 = 8$

4 Jenny and Simon are both thinking of numbers.

I think of a number.
I multiply by 4.
I add 5.
My answer is 25.

Jenny

I think of a number.
I double it.
I subtract 6.
My answer is 10.

Simon

   a **i** Write down an equation for Jenny's number.

       ii Solve your equation.

   b **i** Write down an equation for Simon's number.

       ii What number was Simon thinking of?

5 Rachel buys eight tins of baby food.

   One tin of baby food costs t pence.

   She gets 24 pence change from £4.

   Write an equation for t and solve it.

   Check your answer.

Building skills

Sales forecasting

Toolbox

When you **expand** an expression you multiply out the brackets.
When you rewrite an expression using brackets you are **factorising**.

$$5a + 10 = 5(a + 2)$$

- $5a + 10$ is the expanded expression.
- $5(a + 2)$ is the factorised expression.

When you expand (or multiply out) brackets you must multiply every term inside the bracket by the term outside the bracket.

$$b \times (a + 3b - 2) = b \times a + b \times 3b + b \times -2$$
$$= ab + 3b^2 - 2b$$

> There are three terms inside the bracket so there will be three terms in your answer.

When you factorise an expression, look at the numbers first and then the letters.

$$2fg + 6f^2 = 2 \times fg + 2 \times 3f^2$$
$$= 2f \times g + 2f \times 3f$$
$$= 2f(g + 3f)$$

> 2 goes into 2 and 6.

> f goes into fg and f^2

> so $2f$ goes outside the bracket.

$2f$ is the highest common factor (HCF) of both terms.

Example – Expanding brackets

Expand the brackets in these expressions.

a $3(4a - 7)$

b $t(s - u)$

Solution

a $3(4a - 7) = 3 \times 4a - 3 \times 7$

$= 12a - 21$

> Multiply every term inside the brackets by the term outside the brackets.

b $t(s - u) = t \times s - t \times u$

$= st - tu$

> Remember to use correct algebraic notation. You don't write the × sign and you arrange the letters alphabetically.

Example – Factorising expressions

Factorise these expressions.

a $12x - 18$

b $6y^2 + 2y$

Solution

a $12x - 18 = 6 \times 2x - 6 \times 3$

> 6 goes into $12x$ and 18.

$= 6 \times (2x - 3)$

> Write the 6 outside the brackets. Be careful to keep the minus sign.

$= 6(2x - 3)$

> Remember to use correct algebraic notation. You don't write the × sign.

b $6y^2 + 2y = 2y \times 3y + 2y \times 1$

> 2 and y go into $6y^2$ and $2y$.

$= 2y \times (3y + 1)$

> Don't forget to write the 1 in the brackets.

$= 2y(3y + 1)$

Check: $2y(3y + 1) = 2y \times 3y + 2y \times 1$

$= 6y^2 + 2y$ ✓

Remember:

✦ Write letters in alphabetical order.

✦ Make sure you always factorise fully (so the expression inside the brackets can't be factorised further).

✦ Multiply out brackets to check you have factorised an expression correctly.

Skills practice A

1 Sam is using brackets to help her with multiplication.

> $3 \times 27 = 3 \times (20 + 7)$
> $= 3 \times 20 + 3 \times 7$
> $= 60 + 21$
> $= 81$

Work out these using the same method as Sam.

a 5×23 **b** 6×32 **c** 7×47 **d** 8×84

2 a Malini and Veronica are trying to work out $4 \times (9 + 2)$.

Malini	Veronica
$4 \times (9 + 2) = 4 \times 11$ $=$	$4 \times (9 + 2) = 4 \times 9 + 4 \times 2$ $= 36 + 8$ $=$

Complete their working.

Who's method is quicker in this case?

b Work out these.

   i $7 \times (5 + 2)$ **ii** $(7 \times 5) + 2$ **iii** $3 \times (4 + 6)$

   iv $(3 \times 4) + 6$ **v** $4 \times (9 - 1)$

3 Work out these.

   a $(4 \times 9) - 1$ **b** $(3 + 2) \times (5 - 3)$ **c** $3 + (2 \times 5) - 3$

   d $(2 + 4) \times (4 + 2)$ **e** $(3 + 4) \times (7 - 7)$

4 Work out these by expanding the brackets.

   a $3 \times (5 + 2 + 9)$ **b** $5 \times (10 + 3 - 6)$ **c** $8 \times (12 + 3 - 10)$

   d $2 \times (13 + 7 + 3)$ **e** $5 \times (7 + 2 - 9)$

5 Work out these by expanding the brackets.

   a $5 \times 199 = 5 \times (200 - 1)$ **b** $3 \times 53 = 3 \times (50 + 3)$ **c** $9 \times 99 = 9 \times (100 - 1)$

   d $4 \times 62 = 4 \times (60 + 2)$ **e** $7 \times 19 = 7 \times (20 - 1)$

6 a Find the areas of these rectangles.

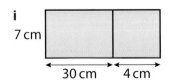

i 7 cm — 30 cm, 4 cm   **ii** 6 cm — 20 cm, 4 cm   **iii** 5 cm — 40 cm, 2 cm

b Use these rectangles to find

   i 6×24 **ii** 5×42 **iii** 7×34

Reasoning

7 a Write down all of the factors of these numbers.
The first one has been done for you.
i 12 has factors 1, 2, 3, 4, 6 and 12.
ii 6   **iii** 18   **iv** 15   **v** 24   **vi** 36

b Write down the highest common factor of these pairs of numbers.
i 6 and 12   **ii** 15 and 18   **iii** 24 and 36

8 Look at these algebra cards.

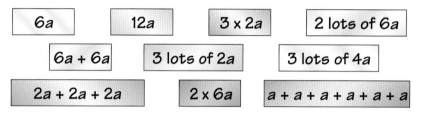

$6a$	$12a$	$3 \times 2a$	2 lots of $6a$
$6a + 6a$	3 lots of $2a$	3 lots of $4a$	
$2a + 2a + 2a$	$2 \times 6a$	$a + a + a + a + a + a$	

a Match the cards with equivalent expressions.
b Check your answers by finding the value of each card when $a = 3$.
c What other ways can you write
i $6a$
ii $12a$?

9 For each of these rectangles
i write down an expression for the area using brackets
ii expand the brackets in your expression
iii find the area when $x = 2$.

a 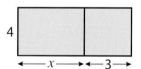   **b** 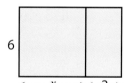   **c**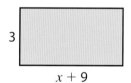

10 Each coloured expression has a matching white expression.
Find the matching pairs.

A $2a + 2$ 2 $2(a + 1)$ C $12d - 4$ 4 $4(3d - 1)$ 5 $3(a + b)$

B $3a + 3b$

1 $3(5a - 8)$ 3 $12(1 + 2b - 3c)$ D $12 + 24b - 36c$ E $15a - 24$

11 Find the value of $2 (l + w)$ when
a $l = 3$ and $w = 7$ **b** $l = 5$ and $w = 5$ **c** $l = 10$ and $w = 2$
d $l = 4$ and $w = 0$ **e** $l = 2$ and $w = 2$ **f** $l = 10$ and $w = 12$
g $l = 5$ and $w = 9$ **h** $l = 8$ and $w = 5$ **i** $l = 18$ and $w = 20$
j $l = 25$ and $w = 50$

Skills practice B

1 Expand the brackets in these expressions.

a $5(2 + c)$ b $3(x - 6)$ c $7(p + q)$

d $4(2d + 3)$ e $4(b + 8)$ f $8(2r - 1)$

g $3(1 - k)$ h $3(1 + 2m - 3n)$ i $5(2a - 3b)$

j $12(2 + 2d + 2e)$ k $2(6u - 8v - 4w - 10x)$ l $6(2y - x - z)$

2 Factorise the following expressions and work out their values.

a $4 \times 3 + 4 \times 5$ b $7 \times 3 - 7 \times 2$ c $2 \times 3 + 5 \times 3$

d $4 \times 5 + 5 \times 5$ e $4 \times 5 - 3 + 5$ f $3 \times 2 + 4 \times 2 + 5 \times 2$

g $7 \times 5 + 7 \times 3 - 7 \times 7$ h $9 \times 5 + 9 \times 3 - 9 \times 4$

3 Simplify these expressions.

Use brackets in your answers where you can.

a $5a + b + 3a + 2b$ b $4c + 5d + 3c + 2d$

c $6x + 5 + 5x + 6$ d $12x + 6y - 10x - 4y$

e $6p + 3q + 4q + 2p + 10p + 11q$ f $3x - 4 - 2 - x + 6x + 8 + x$

g $5x + 4 + 2y - 2x - 6y - 3 + 6x + 8 + 9y - 3x$

4 Factorise these expressions fully.

a $3x + 6$ b $2x + 10$ c $10x + 2$

d $10x - 2$ e $5x + 15$ f $15f - 45$

g $30s - 40$ h $12b + 6a$ i $48 - 24a$

5 Find the values of the following:

a $3(x + y)$ when   i $x = 2$ and $y = 8$ ii $x = 4$ and $y = 1$

                iii $x = 2$ and $y = 0$ iv $x = 5$ and $y = -1$

b $5(x - y)$ when   i $x = 10$ and $y = 8$ ii $x = 10$ and $y = 9$

                iii $x = 10$ and $y = 0$ iv $x = 5$ and $y = 5$

c $(x + y) \times (x - y)$ when   i $x = 5$ and $y = 2$ ii $x = 4$ and $y = 3$

                iii $x = 6$ and $y = 0$ iv $x = 4$ and $y = 1$

d $(a + b + c) \div 3$ when   i $a = 5$, $b = 6$ and $c = 7$ ii $a = 1$, $b = 1$ and $c = 1$

                iii $a = 2$, $b = 1$ and $c = 0$ iv $a = 9$, $b = 6$ and $c = -6$

6 John has $3n - 1$ sweets and Mary has $3(n - 1)$ sweets.

Who has more sweets?

Explain your answer clearly.

7 The area of this rectangle is $(9x + 6)\,\text{cm}^2$.

a Factorise $9x + 6$ fully.

b What is the height of the rectangle?

c What is the length of the rectangle when $x = 2$?

d What is the area of the rectangle when $x = 2$?

? cm

$(3x + 2)\,\text{cm}$

Reasoning

8 The area of this rectangle is $(24y - 30)\,\text{cm}^2$.

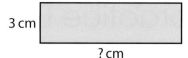

3 cm

? cm

  a Write down all the ways of factorising $24y - 30$.

  b The height of the rectangle is 3 cm.
Write down an expression for the length of the rectangle.

  c The length of the rectangle is 6 cm.
What is the value of y?

  d What is the area of the rectangle when $y = 2$?

9 Expand the brackets and simplify these expressions.

  a $5(b - 2) + 4(2 - b)$ **b** $3(d + 2) - 2(d - 1)$

10 Expand the brackets in these expressions.

  a $3(a - b)$ **b** $5(3x + 8y)$ **c** $x(x - 1)$

  d $x(x + 5)$ **e** $2x(x + 5)$ **f** $2x(3x + 5)$

  g $x(x + y)$ **h** $4x(x - y)$ **i** $4x(5x - 7y)$

  j $x(x^2 - x - 1)$ **k** $3x^2(2x + 5)$ **l** $3x^2(4x - 11y)$

11 Factorise these expressions fully.

  a $5x + 15$ **b** $14a + 21b$ **c** $xy + xz$

  d $5xy + 10xz$ **e** $3x - ax$ **f** $ax^2 + bx^2$

  g $x^2 - xy$ **h** $x^2 - 5xy$ **i** $5y + y^2$

  j $x^3 + x^2 - x$ **k** $x^4 + x^2$ **l** $x^4 - 9x^2$

12 Look at the expressions below.
Some are in factorised form, others in expanded form.
Find the matching pairs.
Write them in two columns, with the expanded form on the left and its factorised form on the right beside it.
One of the expressions cannot be factorised.

$x^2 + xy$
$x(x + 1)$
$xy + y^2$
$x(x - y)$
$x^3 + x^2 + x$
$x^2 + 1$
$x^2 + x$

$x(x + y)$
$x(x^2 + x + 1)$
$y(x + y)$
$x^2 - xy$

13 Expand the brackets in these expressions and then simplify your answers.
If you can factorise an answer, do so.

  a $3(x + y) + 2(x + 2y)$ **b** $3(x - y) + 4(x + y)$

  c $3(x + y) + 4(x - y)$ **d** $5(2a + b) - 3(a - 3b)$

  e $3(2a + b) - 2(a - b)$ **f** $8(a + 2b) - 3(a - 8b)$

14 Look at how Sam factorises the expression $24x^2y - 18xy$.

Factorise these expressions fully.

a $18d^2 + 3d$ **b** $6e^2 - 2e$

c $9f^2g - 6fg$ **d** $24g^2h + 6g$

e $15h^3j - 5h^2$

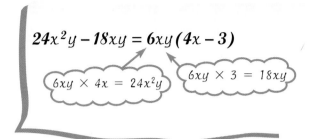

$$24x^2y - 18xy = 6xy(4x - 3)$$

$6xy \times 4x = 24x^2y$ $6xy \times 3 = 18xy$

Wider skills practice

1 a Write an expression using a bracket for the area of this rectangle.

  b Expand the brackets.

  c The area of the rectangle is $72\,\text{cm}^2$.

    i Write an equation using your expression.

    ii Solve your equation to find the value of p.

2 a Write an expression for the perimeter of this triangle.

  b Expand the brackets and simplify your answer.

  c The perimeter of the triangle is $39\,\text{cm}$.

    i Write an equation using your expression.

    ii Solve your equation to find the value of b.

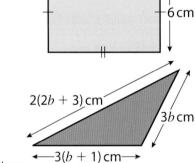

3 Chinua is planning to make this garden pond in Design and Technology.
It consists of metal rods joined together.
They are then covered in a strong waterproof fabric.

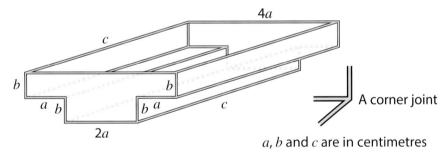

A corner joint

a, b and c are in centimetres

  a Find expressions for

    i the length of metal rod

    ii the area of fabric

    iii the volume of the pond

    iv the number of corner joints.

    Most of your answers will involve the letters a, b and c and you should give them in factorised form.

  b Find the values of the four quantities in part **a** when $a = 40$, $b = 30$ and $c = 200$.
State the units for each answer.

  c Ruth tells Chinua, 'You should make a and b the same.'
Give the four expressions in part **a** now, using the letters a and c.
They should be in factorised form where possible.

  d Find the values of the expressions in part **c** when $a = 40$ and $c = 150$.

Applying skills

1 Try Karl's 'mind reading' trick.

Karl's friend Nina says her answer is 80.

  a What number did Nina think of?

  b What rule does Karl use to find the number?

  c Show why this trick works.

> *Think of a number between 1 and 9 and add 3. Multiply your answer by 5 and subtract 6. Now double your answer and subtract 18. What is your answer?*

Karl

2 a Luka has been selling things he does not want for a while on eBay, but recently he has branched out and has been raiding his local junk shops to buy old books, which he has been selling online.

Book	Cost price	Selling price
1	25p	£2.30
2	£1.20	£3.50
3	£2.10	£5.00
4	£3.00	£4.80
5	£1.50	£2.90

How much profit was Luka left with after he paid the shops?

b Luka's book selling is getting more successful and he is selling about 100 books a week. It is taking him ages to keep working out his profit by hand. He decides to set up a proper spreadsheet, but before he can do that, he has to write down how he calculates the profit for a book in words. What could he write?

c Now it is time to use algebra to help. If the cost of a book is C and the price he sells it for is D, how does he calculate his profit, E?

d To make life difficult, Luka agrees to give some of his profit to his mother as he is using her computer and broadband to do his deals and she is posting his books for him! They agree she will have one quarter of the profit. How does Luka calculate how much money he gets to keep now?

e Luka sets up a spreadsheet to calculate the money he keeps. He thinks he made a mistake. What has he done wrong and how can he put it right?

	F2		fx	=D2-C2*3/4		
A	B		C	Selling Price	Profit	Money to keep
1	Name of book		Cost			
2	1 War and Peace		£3.78	£5.89	£2.11	£3.06
3	2 Happy Jack		£0.20	£1.56	£1.36	£1.41
4	3 Little and Large		£1.70	£2.45	£0.75	£1.18
5	4 The Seaside		£0.30	£1.20	£0.90	£0.98
6	5 Dinosaurs and Lizards		£0.45	£2.50	£2.05	£2.16
7	6 Maths for mums and dads		£2.34	£3.99	£1.65	£2.24
8	7 Soduko - trade secrets		£1.34	£2.01	£0.67	£1.01

Pause for thought

Luka is doing well with his book selling, but would you have any advice for him as the business grows?

Reviewing skills

1 Expand the brackets in these expressions.

   a $5(w + 2)$ **b** $4(m + n)$ **c** $3(x + 2y)$

   d $6(2 - 3r)$ **e** $2(6 - 9r) + 3(4 - 6r)$ **f** $2(p - 2q + 5)$

   g $7(a + 3b - c - 4)$ **h** $3x(4x - 7)$ **i** $2p^2(pq - 2q)$

2 Here are some Algebra snap cards. Match the expressions.

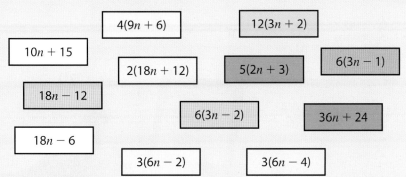

3 Factorise these expressions fully.

   a $6a^2 + ab$ **b** $15ab + 10a$ **c** $16cd - 12d^2$

   d $6a + 6b$ **e** $5b + 10$ **f** $8c - 12$

4 Find the values of the following.

   a $3(x + 2y)$ **i** when $x = 4$ and $y = 1$ **ii** when $x = 1$ and $y = 4$

   b $(x + y) \times (x - y)$ **i** when $x = 5$ and $y = 1$ **ii** when $x = 7$ and $y = 7$

   c $(x + 1) \div (y + 1)$ **i** when $x = 3$ and $y = 1$ **ii** when $x = 1$ and $y = 3$

5 Match the words with the algebra. One expression in words and one expression in algebra do not match. Write a matching expression for each of them.

Multiply b by 2 then subtract from a	$a(b - c)$
Subtract c from a then multiply by b	$\dfrac{a}{c} - b$
Add b to a then divide into c	$\dfrac{ab}{c}$
Multiply a by b then divide by c	$\dfrac{c}{a + b}$
Divide c by b then multiply by a	abc
Multiply a by c then divide into b	$b(a - c)$
Add b to a then divide by c	$a - 2b$
Multiply ab by c	$\dfrac{b}{ac}$
Multiply a by 4 then subtract c	$\dfrac{a + b}{c}$
Subtract c from b then multiply by a	$\dfrac{c}{b} \times a$

Building skills

Example outside the Maths classroom

Working to deadlines

Toolbox

You can use the **balance method** to solve equations with an unknown on both sides.
The first step is to get all the unknowns onto the same side of the equation:

$3x + 8 = 33 - 2x$

$+ 2x$ $+ 2x$

| The inverse of subtract $2x$ is add $2x$. |

| Remember to do the same, thing to both sides of the equation so it balances. |

$5x + 8 = 33$

| The inverse of add 8 is subtract 8. |

$- 8$ $- 8$

| Subtract 8 from both sides of the equation. |

$5x = 25$

| The inverse of multiply by 5 is divide by 5. |

$\div 5$ $\div 5$

| Divide both sides by 5. |

$x = 5$

Check: $15 + 8 = 33 - 10 = 23$ ✓

| Always check your work. |

Example – Solving an equation with an unknown on both sides

Solve $3x - 8 = 20 - x$.

Solution

$3x - 8 = 20 - x$

$4x - 8 = 20$ ⟵ **Add x to both sides.**

$4x = 28$ ⟵ **Add 8 to both sides.**

$x = 7$ ⟵ **Divide both sides by 4.**

Check: $3x - 8 = 20 - x$

$3 \times 7 - 8 = 20 - 7$

$21 - 8 = 13$

$13 = 13$ ✓

Example – Solving word problems

Jamie and Holly both had the same amount of credit on their mobile phones.

Jamie sent 18 texts and has £1.40 credit left.

Holly sent 12 texts and has £2 credit left.

They both pay the same amount for one text.

a Find the cost of one text message.

b How much credit did Jamie and Holly start with?

Solution

a Let t represent the cost of one text message in pence. Change pounds to pence because whole numbers are easier to work with.

Jamie's credit = Holly's credit

$18t + 140 = 12t + 200$ ⟵ **Subtract $12t$ from both sides.**

$6t + 140 = 200$ ⟵ **Subtract 140 from both sides.**

$6t = 60$ ⟵ **Divide both sides by 6.**

$t = 10$

So a text message costs 10p.

b Substitute $t = 10$ into the expression for Jamie's credit.

$18t + 140 = 18 \times 10 + 140$

$= 320$

So Jamie's starting credit was 320p or £3.20

Check that Holly's credit is also 320p:

$12t + 200 = 12 \times 10 + 200$

$= 320$ ✓

Remember:

✦ The equation must balance: always do the same to both sides.
✦ If you divide both sides of an equation by, say 2, make sure you divide every term by 2.
✦ If you multiply both sides of an equation by, say 2, make sure you multiply every term by 2.
✦ Always check your solution by substituting back into the original equation.

Skills practice A

1 Alexandra is weighing some tins of soup using scales.
The soup tins are all the same.

Each weighs m kg.
Alexandra writes:

$4m + 5 = 2m + 6$

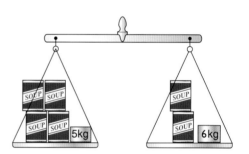

a Solve Alexandra's equation to find the weight of one tin of soup.

b Check you have solved the equation correctly.

c What is the total weight on the left-hand side of the scales?

2 Write down an equation to match each balance problem.
For example the equation for part **a** is $2x = 12$.
Solve your equations to find the mass of one coloured cylinder in each case.

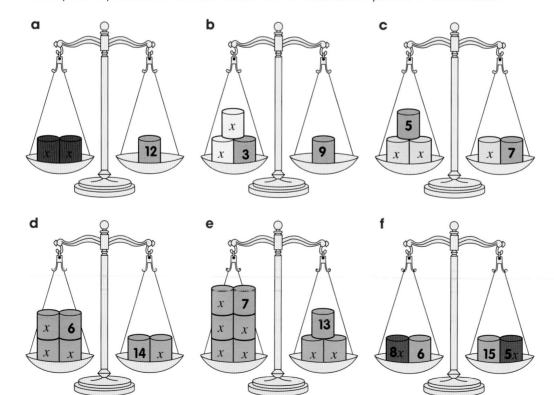

3 Solve each of these equations.

Make sure that each side of the equation balances the other.

Check each of your solutions.

a $5a = 15$ **b** $10 - b = 7$ **c** $7 = c - 8$

d $\dfrac{d}{4} = 5$ **e** $19 = 6 + e$ **f** $3f + 6 = 15$

g $12 + 2g = 16$ **h** $2 = 7h - 5$ **i** $10 - 3i = 4$

4 Solve these equations.

Check each of your solutions by substituting back into the original equation.

a $3a + 4 = 2a + 7$ **b** $7b - 5 = 6b + 1$ **c** $4c + 3 = 2c + 5$

d $2d - 4 = 8 - d$ **e** $6e + 3 = 12 - 3e$ **f** $7f - 2 = 4f + 7$

g $3 + 2g = 13 - 3g$ **h** $10 - h = 16 - 3h$

Skills practice B

1 Solve these equations.

a $2n + 1 = n + 3$ **b** $3p - 2 = 2p + 1$ **c** $1 + 4r = 2r + 5$

d $3b - 2 = 4 + b$ **e** $10 + 2f = 15 - 3f$ **f** $3 + 3w = 10 - 4w$

g $5k - 1 = 2k + 2$ **h** $15 - x = 23 - 2x$ **i** $12 - 3c = 18 - 5c$

j $4m - 3 = 5 + 2m$

2 Harry is buying some pencils from the local shop.

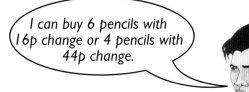

I can buy 6 pencils with 16p change or 4 pencils with 44p change.

Harry

a Write down an expression (use p for the cost in pence of one pencil) for the cost of buying

   i six pencils and having 16p change

   ii four pencils and having 44p change.

b Form an equation with your two expressions by making them equal.

c Solve your equation to find the cost of one pencil.

Check you have solved the equation correctly.

d How much money does Harry have?

Reasoning

3 Mercy is buying some bananas on holiday.

I can buy five bananas and I'll have 10 cents left over. Or I can buy three bananas and I'll have 50 cents left over.

Mercy

a Write an equation using this information.
b Solve your equation to find the cost of one banana,
Check your answer.
c How much money does Mercy have?

4 Andrew and Brad are having an argument about this equation.

$$7x - 8 = 19 - 2x$$

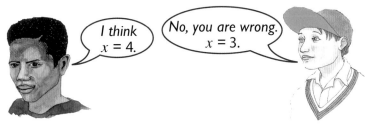

I think x = 4.

No, you are wrong. x = 3.

Andrew   Brad

a How can you check who is right?
b Who is right?
c Show how to solve the equation.
Explain your method at each stage.

5 Solve these equations.
a $2.1x + 0.4 = 1.1x + 2.4$
b $3.1x + 0.4 = 1.1x + 2.4$
c $2.4x + 3.9 = 9.9 + 0.4x$
d $2.9x - 0.5 = 3.1 + 0.9x$
e $10.4x + 12 = 36 - 1.6x$

Wider skills practice

Reasoning

1 Peter is the penguin keeper at Avonford Zoo.
He is designing a new enclosure for the penguins.
It must fit around the penguin pond.
Here are his two designs.
The measurements are in metres.

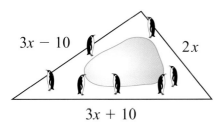

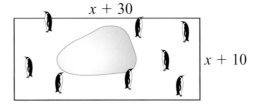

a Write expressions for the perimeters of the enclosures.
Simplify your expressions.

b Both penguin enclosures use the same length of fencing.
Write an equation for x.

c Solve your equation to find x.

d What are the dimensions of each penguin enclosure?

e How much fencing will Peter need for each enclosure?

Reasoning

2 Find the area of this rectangle.

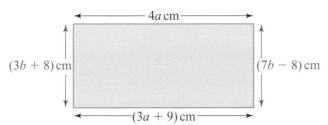

Reasoning

3 Jamie and Holly spend the same amount of time exercising at the youth club.
Jamie spends 1 hour playing table tennis and does some swimming.
Holly only goes swimming. She swims for four times longer than Jamie.

a How long does Jamie spend swimming?

b How long does Holly spend swimming?

4

One small tile weighs $\frac{1}{2}$ a kilogram.
Eight small tiles and 6 large tiles weigh 16 kg.
What is the weight of one large tile?

Jack

Write an equation to solve Jack's puzzle.

5

I think of a number.
I multiply it by 3 and subtract 6. This gives the same answer as when I subtract my number from 30.
What is my number?

Megan

What is Megan's number?

Applying skills

1 Janice hires a car for a day. Her bill comes to £82.40.
Let *m* stand for the number of miles she drove.
Write down an equation involving *m* and use it to find how many miles Janice drove.

CAR HIRE
£50 per day
+
40p per mile

2 A coach party of 50 people are going to a zoo.
The total entrance cost for the whole group is £256.
Let *n* stand for the number of children in the group.

   a Write down an expression for the number of adults in the group.

   b Write down an equation involving *n*.

   c Solve your equation to find the number of children and the number of adults in the group.

ZOO ENTRANCE

Adults..........£6
Children.......£4

Reviewing skills

1 Solve these equations and check your answers.

   a $3x - 2 = 4x - 5$ b $2x + 9 = 3x - 5$ c $4x + 6 = 8 + 3x$

   d $7x - 8 = 4x + 4$ e $5x - 5 = 2x + 4$ f $7 + 3x = 4x + 2$

   g $3 + 7x = 7 + 3x$ h $5x + 1 = 6x - 1$ i $6x - 10 = 4x$

2 Paul thinks of a number, x.

I think of a number. I multiply it by 4 and add 2. The answer is four more than twice my number.

Paul

   a Write down expressions for

      i   'multiply my number by 4 and add 2'

      ii   'four more than twice my number'.

   b Form an equation.

   c Solve your equation to find Paul's mystery number.

Building skills

Brainteasers

Toolbox

When an equation has a bracket it is usually easiest to expand the brackets first.

$$5(3x - 6) = 12$$

$$5 \times 3x - 5 \times 6 = 12$$ ⟵ **First multiply out the brackets.**

$$15x - 30 = 12$$ ⟵ **Add 30 to both sides.**

$$15x = 42$$ ⟵ **Divide both sides by 15.**

$$x = 2.8$$

Alternatively you can choose to divide both sides of the equation by the number outside the brackets.

$$4(n + 13) = 80$$

$$n + 13 = 20$$ ⟵ **Divide both sides by 4.**

$$n = 7$$ ⟵ **Subtract 13 from both sides.**

Example – Solving equations with an unknown on one side

Solve these equations.

a $6(5a - 2) = 33$ **b** $5(4b + 3) = -25$

Solution

a $6(5a - 2) = 33$

$6 \times 5a - 6 \times 2 = 33$ ⟵ **First multiply out the brackets.**

$30a - 12 = 33$ ⟵ **Simplify.**

$30a = 45$ ⟵ **Add 12 to both sides.**

$a = 1.5$ ⟵ **Divide both sides by 30.**

b $5(4b + 3) = -25$

$4b + 3 = -5$ ⟵ **It is easiest to divide both sides by 5 first.**

$4b = -8$ ⟵ **Subtract 3 from both sides.**

$b = -2$ ⟵ **Divide both sides by 4.**

Example – Solving equations with an unknown on both sides

Solve $2(3 - x) = 9 + x$.

Solution

$$2(3 - x) = 9 + x$$

$$2 \times 3 - 2 \times x = 9 + x$$ ← First multiply out the brackets.

$$6 - 2x = 9 + x$$ ← You can subtract x from both sides or add $2x$ to both sides.

$$6 = 9 + 3x$$ ← Subtracting x from both sides gives a negative x term so it is easier add $2x$ to both sides.

$$-3 = 3x$$ ← Subtract 9 from both sides.

$$-1 = x$$ ← Divide both sides by 3.

$$x = -1$$ ← Swap the two sides of the equation over. $-1 = x$ means the same as $x = -1$.

Check by substituting $x = -1$ back into the original equation.

$$2(3 - x) = 9 + x$$
$$2 \times (3 - -1) = 9 + -1$$ ✓
$$2 \times 4 = 8$$

Remember:

✦ Multiply every term inside the bracket by the term outside the bracket.
✦ Check your solution by substituting it back into the original equation.
✦ When there is an unknown on both sides gather all the unknowns on one side.

Skills practice A

1 Solve these equations by expanding the brackets first.
   Check each of your solutions by substituting back into the original equation.
   a $4(w + 2) = 14$ **b** $5(x - 3) = 11$ **c** $10(7 - y) = 16$
   d $8 = 5(2z - 4)$

2 Solve these equations by dividing both sides by the number outside of the brackets first.
   Check each of your solutions by substituting back into the original equation.
   a $4(q + 3) = 20$ **b** $6(r - 7) = 18$ **c** $2 = 2(3s - 8)$
   d $5(6 - t) = 15$ **e** $8(5 - x) = 40$

3 Solve these equations by expanding the brackets first.

Check each of your solutions by substituting back into the original equation.

    a $5(2a + 1) = 17$ **b** $4(3 + 2b) = 52$ **c** $7(12 - 2c) = 28$

    d $6(2d - 1) = 3$ **e** $10(8 - 4e) = 0$

4 Ali is thinking of a number.

I think of a number.
I double it and subtract 6.
When I multiply the result
by 3 the answer is 24.

Ali

    a Copy and complete the following table to build up an equation for Ali's number.

Instruction	Algebra
I think of a number … n	n
Double it …	
Subtract 6 …	
Multiply the result by 3 …	
The answer is 24.	

    b Solve your equation to work out Ali's number.

    c Show how you can check your solution is right.

5 **a** Aloke and Shonali are solving the equation $3(x + 4) = 18$.

      Here is the start of their working.

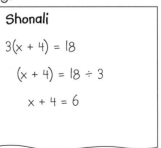

Aloke

$3(x + 4) = 18$

$3x + 12 = 18$

$3x = 18 - 12$

$3x = 6$

Shonali

$3(x + 4) = 18$

$(x + 4) = 18 \div 3$

$x + 4 = 6$

Complete their working.

    b Use both methods to solve these equations.

      i $4(d + 2) = 20$ **ii** $5(h - 3) = 15$ **iii** $5(x + 4) = 20$

      iv $2(3x + 1) = 20$ **v** $3(2m - 4) = 12$

6 Solve these equations.

a $7(b + 2) - 3b = 18$ **b** $4(3x - 2) - 7x = 2$ **c** $2(5a - 3) + 8 - 4a = 44$

d $3(p + 2) + 2p = 36$ **e** $5(q - 1) - 4q = 9$

7 Solve these equations.

a $2(b + 3) = 7b + 1$ **b** $5(f - 1) = 4f + 1$ **c** $4(2e - 3) = 6e + 2$

d $4(2a + 1) = 5a + 7$ **e** $5(3n - 2) = 10n$

Skills practice B

1 Solve these equations.

a $4(2e + 3) = 7e + 2$ **b** $5(3n - 2) = 10n$ **c** $2(b + 3) = b + 7$

d $3(x + 1) = 2x + 5$ **e** $5(x - 4) = 2x + 1$

2 Solve these equations.

a $3(x + 2) = 2(x + 3)$ **b** $5(x + 2) = 2(x + 20)$ **c** $10(x + 1) = 5(x + 3)$

d $7(x - 1) = 2(x + 4)$ **e** $3(3g - 8) = 2g - 3$

3 Oliver and Susan are trying to solve this equation
$$10n - 18 = 2(7 - 3n)$$

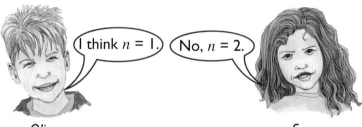

I think $n = 1$.

No, $n = 2$.

Oliver   *Susan*

a Without solving the equation check who is right.

b Solve the equation showing your working.

4 Solve each of these equations and write down the corresponding letter from the table.
What word do you spell?

7	–7	$\frac{1}{2}$	8	10	–6	0	–4	2
P	E	R	D	G	T	U	A	S

a $\frac{3x}{14} = \frac{3}{7}$ **b** $6(x - 2) = 5x - 12$ **c** $3(x - 2) = 5(x - 4)$

d $3(x + 8) = -x - 4$ **e** $3(2x + 1) = 0$

5 Solve these equations.

a $\frac{x}{5} = 4$ **b** $\frac{x}{4} = 5$ **c** $\frac{1}{4}(x + 1) = 5$

d $\frac{1}{4}(x - 1) = 5$ **e** $\frac{1}{4}(2x - 3) = 2$

Wider skills practice

Reasoning

1 a Find an expression for the perimeter of this rectangle.

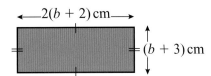

b The perimeter of the rectangle is 32 cm.
Write down an equation for this information.

c Solve your equation to find the value of b.

d What are the length and width of the rectangle?

Reasoning

2 Find the area of this square.

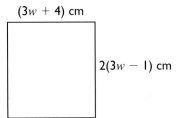

3 a Try solving these equations.

  i $4(x + 2) + 2x = 6x + 8$

  ii $6x - 2(2x + 1) = 2x - 2$

  iii $12x + 9 = 3(4x + 3)$

  What happens? Why does this happen?

b An **identity** says 'this expression always equals that expression no matter what values are chosen for the variables'.
We use ≡ instead of = to show that the two expressions are always equal.
Complete these identities.

  i $5(x + 1) \equiv \boxed{}\, x + \boxed{}$

  ii $x + x + x + x \equiv \boxed{}\, x$

  iii $2(x - 2) - 2x + 6 \equiv \boxed{}$

  iv $x^2 \times x^3 \equiv x^{\boxed{}}$

c Show that each identity in part **b** is true for three different values of x.

d Put each of these algebra cards in the column that best describes it.

| $V = IR$ | $4n - 1 = 7$ | $y = 2x + 1$ | $4p - 1$ | $A = \frac{1}{2}\,bh$ |

| $x \rightarrow 2x - 3$ | $3(a + 1) \equiv 3a + 3$ | $A = \pi r^2$ | $c + c + c \equiv 3c$ | $3(y + 1) = 2(y + 5)$ |

Expression	Equation	Identity	Formula	Function

Applying skills

Reasoning

1 Look at this two-way function machine.

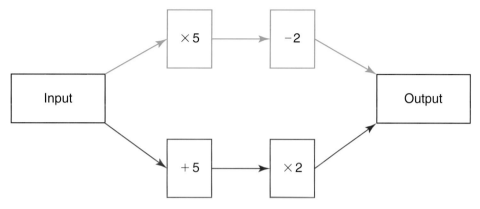

a Find the input which gives the same output whichever path you take on the function machine.

b Design your own two-way function machine that gives the same output either way round for:

i exactly one input

ii two inputs

iii all inputs

Problem solving

2 The head of a fish is 6 cm long.

The body of the fish is twice as long as the head and tail together.

In total, the fish is 54 cm long.

How long is the tail?

Problem solving

3 A farmer has 40 fewer cows than she has sheep.

She has twice as many hens as she has sheep.

The total number of animals on her farm is six times the number of cows.

How many of each type of animal does she have?

Problem solving

4 Look at what Julian says.

In seven years time I will be twice as old as I was three years ago.

Julian

How old is Julian now?

Reviewing skills

1   Solve these equations.

   a $4(k + 2) = 24$ **b** $7(6 - 2r) = 28$ **c** $5t + 8 = 2(2t + 9)$

   d $3(n - 1) = 3 - 3n$ **e** $4(g + 1) = 3(g + 3)$

2   Solve these equations.

   a $2(p - 2) = p - 1$ **b** $3(x + 2) = 2x + 13$ **c** $3(2 - 3r) + 2 = 2(5 - r)$

   d $3(2h - 3) = 3 + 4h$ **e** $2(5 - k) = 4(3 - k)$

Building skills

 Example outside the Maths classroom

Designing platform games

 Toolbox

These are the **laws of indices**.

$$a^n = \underbrace{a \times a \times a \times \dots \times a}_{n \text{ factors of } a}$$

$$\text{So } a^5 = \underbrace{a \times a \times a \times a \times a}_{5 \text{ factors of } a}$$

$$a^1 = a$$

$$a^0 = 1$$

$$a^x \times a^y = a^{x+y} \qquad \text{So } a^5 \times a^7 = a^{5+7} = a^{12}$$

$$a^x \div a^y = a^{x-y} \qquad \text{So } a^9 \div a^4 = a^{9-4} = a^5$$

$$(a^x)^y = a^{x \times y} \qquad \text{So } (a^5)^3 = a^{5 \times 3} = a^{15}$$

When you expand a pair of brackets you multiply every term in the second bracket by every term in the first bracket then simplify your answer.

$$(x + 5)(x - 3) = x \times x + x \times (-3) + 5 \times x + 5 \times (-3)$$

$$= x^2 + (-3x) + (+5x) + (-15)$$

$$= x^2 + 2x - 15$$

$$= x^2 + 2x - 15$$

Alternatively, you can use a table

	$x + 5$	
x	x^2	$5x$
-3	$-3x$	-15

$$x^2 + 5x - 3x - 15$$
$$= x^2 + 2x - 15$$

Example – Simplify harder expressions

Simplify these expressions.

a $2a^3b^7 \times 4ab^5$

b $\dfrac{12a^4b^3}{4ab^2}$

Solution

a Use the rules of indices: $a^x \times a^y = a^{x+y}$

$2 \times 4 = 8$

$a^3 \times a = a^3 \times a^1 = a^{3+1} = a^4$

$b^7 \times b^5 = b^{7+5} = b^{12}$

So, $2a^3b^7 \times 4ab^5 = 8a^4b^{12}$

b Use the rules of indices: $a^x \div a^y = a^{x-y}$

$12 \div 4 = 3$

$a^4 \div a = a^4 \div a^1 = a^{4-1} = a^3$

$b^3 \div b^2 = b^{3-2} = b^1 = b$

So, $\dfrac{12a^4b^3}{4ab^2} = 3a^3b$

Example – Expanding a pair of brackets

Expand $(x-4)(x-2)$.

Solution

You can use a grid to help you.

	x	-4
x	x^2	$-4x$
-2	$-2x$	8

Put the contents of one bracket along the top and the other down the side then multiply at each cross-section.

$(x-4)(x-2) = x^2 - 4x - 2x + 8$
$= x^2 - 6x - 8$

Then add the results.

Remember:

✦ When you expand a pair of brackets, take care with the signs.
✦ Use a grid or looping arrows so you don't miss out any terms.

Skills practice A

1 Write these as single powers.
The first one has been done for you.

a $6 \times 6 \times 6 \times 6 \times 6 = 6^5$
b $5 \times 5 \times 5 \times 5 \times 5 \times 5$
c 4×4
d $3 \times 3 \times 3$
e $8 \times 8 \times 8 \times 8$
f $10 \times 10 \times 10 \times 10 \times 10 \times 10$

2 Write these as single powers.
The first one has been done for you.

a $a \times a = a^2$
b $b \times b \times b \times b$
c $c \times c \times c \times c \times c$
d $d \times d \times d$
e $f \times f \times f \times f \times f \times f$
f $g \times g \times g \times g \times g \times g$

3 Write each of these in index form and work out its value.

a $3^2 \times 3$
b $3^2 \times 3^2$
c $3^5 \times 3^2$
d $3^7 \div 3^3$
e $3^6 \div 3^2$
f $3^9 \div 3^6$

4 Copy and complete these algebra pyramids.
The value in each brick is found by multiplying the values in the two bricks underneath it.

a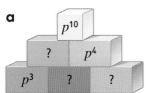

b

5 Copy and complete these algebra pyramids.
The value in each brick is found by multiplying the values in the two bricks underneath it.

a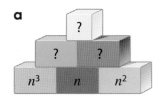

b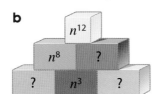

c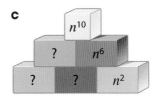

6 You can use a grid to help you expand (multiply out) a pair of brackets.

a i Copy and complete this grid to expand $(x + 5)(x + 4)$.

	x	4
x	x^2	
5		20

ii Add together the four terms inside the grid and simplify your expression.

b Use these grids to help you expand the expressions.

i $(x + 2)(x + 3)$

	x	2
x		
3		

ii $(x + 2)(x + 1)$

	x	2
x		
1		

iii $(x + 1)(x - 2)$

	x	1
x		
-2		

iv $(x \quad 3)(x + 2)$

	x	-3
x		
2		

Skills practice B

1 Write these expressions as single powers.

a $a^6 \times a^3$ **b** $b^7 \times b^2$ **c** $c^5 \times c^4$

d $d^{50} \times d$ **e** $e^6 \div e^4$ **f** $f^6 \div f^2$

g $g^{10} \div g^{10}$ **h** $h^{50} \div h^{49}$ **i** $i^3 \times i^4$

j $j^2 \times j^2$ **k** $k^{15} \times k^{20}$ **l** $l^5 \times l$

m $m^5 \div m^2$ **n** $n^5 \div n$ **o** $p^{50} \div p^{49}$

p $q^{100} \div q^{100}$

2 Jake simplifies $4x^3 \times 5x^2$ like this

$$4x^3 \times 5x^2 = 4 \times 5 \times x^3 \times x^2$$
$$= 20x^5$$

Simplify these expressions.

a $6a^3 \times 3a^5$ **b** $9b^7 \times 6b^5$ **c** $3c^5 \times 2c^9$

d $30d^{40} \times 20d^{60}$

3 Simplify these expressions.

a $2a^5 \times 5a^7$ **b** $3b^4 \times 2b$ **c** $6c^3 \times 2c^{10}$

d $5d^4 \times 2d^0$

4 Simplify these expressions.

a $5a^2b \times 3ab$ **b** $7bc^2 \times 6b^5c^3$ **c** $4c^3d^2 \times 3cd$

d $3de \times 2d^2e^6$ **e** $9ef^6 \times 4e^2f^3$ **f** $10f^{100}g^{50} \times 7f^{75}g^{25}$

5 Laila simplifies $\dfrac{12b^5}{4b^3}$ like this

$$\frac{12}{4} = 3$$

$$\frac{b^5}{b^3} = \frac{b \times b \times b \times b \times b}{b \times b \times b}$$

$$= b^2$$

$$\text{So } \frac{12b^5}{4b^3} = 3b^2$$

Simplify these expressions.

a $\dfrac{15a^6}{3a^4}$ **b** $\dfrac{24b^8}{8b^3}$ **c** $\dfrac{150c^{27}}{15c^9}$

d $\dfrac{125d^{10}}{5d}$ **e** $\dfrac{3ef^3}{ef^2}$ **f** $\dfrac{12fg^2}{3fg}$

g $\dfrac{8g^{10}}{4g^{10}}$ **h** $\dfrac{4gh^6}{2gh^0}$

6 The expression in the top brick of each of these algebra pyramids is found by multiplying together the expressions in the two bricks beneath it.

Copy and complete each algebra pyramid.

Expand and simplify the expression in each of the top bricks.

a
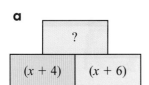

b
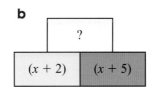

c
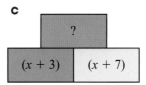

7 Expand these expressions.

i $(x + 2)(x + 6)$ **ii** $(x + 3)(x + 7)$ **iii** $(x + 2)(x - 6)$ **iv** $(x - 3)(x - 7)$

8 Expand the brackets in these expressions.
Simplify your answers.

a $(a + 1)(a + 2)$ **b** $(b + 1)(b + 3)$ **c** $(c + 3)(c - 2)$

d $(d - 2)(d - 5)$ **e** $(e - 2)(e + 7)$ **f** $(f - 9)(f - 4)$

9 Vaya and Sarah have both expanded the expression $(b + 3)^2$.

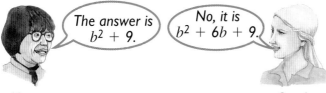

The answer is $b^2 + 9$.

No, it is $b^2 + 6b + 9$.

Vaya   *Sarah*

a Who is right?

b How would you show the other person that she is wrong?

c Expand and simplify these expressions.

i $(n + 3)^2$ **ii** $(x - 3)^2$ **iii** $(y - 30)^2$

Wider skills practice

1 a What does 37^2 mean?

b What does x^2 mean?

c What does $(x + 7)^2$ mean?

d Expand $(x + 7)^2$.

e Use your answer to part **d** to work out 37^2.
What value of x should you use?

f Use this method to calculate **i** 42^2 **ii** 109^2 **iii** 310^2

2 Meena's Dad poses her a problem.

Meena, what is $(3\frac{1}{2})^2$?

That is easy,
I have a special trick for squaring halves.
One more than 3 is 4 so you do 3 times
4 and then add $\frac{1}{4}$. The answer is $12\frac{1}{4}$.

Dad

Meena

a Is Meena correct?

b Check Meena's method for these fractions.

> **i** $\left(1\frac{1}{2}\right)^2$ **ii** $\left(2\frac{1}{2}\right)^2$ **iii** $\left(5\frac{1}{2}\right)^2$ **iv** $\left(10\frac{1}{2}\right)^2$

c By writing $\left(1\frac{1}{2}\right)^2$ as $\left(1+\frac{1}{2}\right)^2$ and multiplying out the brackets show how the rule works.

d By using x to represent any positive integer, show this rule always works

3 a Follow these instructions.

Step 1: Think of two numbers that add up to 1.

Step 2: Square the larger and add this to the smaller number.

Step 3: Square the smaller and add this to the larger number.

b Repeat for other pairs of values that add up to 1.

c Use algebra to explain your results.

4 a Expand these expressions.

> **i** $(a+3)(a-3)$ **ii** $(a+7)(a-7)$ **iii** $(a+b)(a-b)$

What do you notice?

b Expressions in the form $a^2 - b^2$ are often called **the difference of two squares**.
Why do you think this is?

c Factorise these expressions.

> **i** $a^2 - 16$ **ii** $a^2 - 36$ **iii** $a^2 - 64$
> **iv** $a^2 - 1$

d Show how you would use the difference of two squares to work out these calculations without using a calculator.

> **i** $26^2 - 16^2$ **ii** $378^2 - 376^2$ **iii** $1025^2 - 1024^2$

Applying skills

1 Find as many different expressions as you can for the blue area in this square.

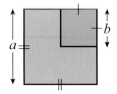

Show algebraically that your expressions are equivalent.

Problem solving

2 a Find as many different expressions as you can for the yellow shaded area in this square.
Show algebraically that your expressions are equivalent.
Hint: Expand the brackets and simplify.

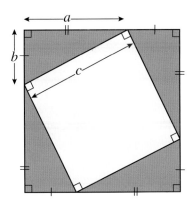

b Which famous theorem have you proved?

Problem solving

3 Copy and complete these algebra pyramids.
The expression in the top brick is found by multiplying the expressions in the two bricks underneath it.
What rules should you use to find the expressions in the bottom bricks?

a

$x^2 + 9x + 20$	
$(x + 4)$	$(x + ?)$

b

$x^2 + 5x + 6$	
$(x + 2)$	$(x + ?)$

c

$x^2 + 8x + 12$	
$(x + 2)$	?

d

$x^2 + 13x + 40$	
$(x + ?)$	$(x + ?)$

e

$x^2 + 11x + 10$	
$(x + ?)$	$(x + ?)$

f

$x^2 + 2x + 1$	
?	?

Reviewing skills

1 Simplify these expressions.
  a $a^3 \times a^4$ **b** $3b^5 \times 4b$ **c** $2c^3 \times 5c^4$

2 Simplify these expressions.
  a $a^4b \times ab$ **b** $2bc^3 \times 5b^2c^5$

3 Simplify these expressions.
  a $\dfrac{12a^2}{2a}$ **b** $\dfrac{b^8c^4}{b^5c^2}$ **c** $\dfrac{24b^6c^3}{4b^4c^3}$

4 Expand the brackets in these expressions.
  a $(a + 3)(a + 5)$ **b** $(b + 5)(b + 5)$ **c** $(c + 3)(c - 2)$
  d $(d - 2)(d - 1)$ **e** $(e - 1)(e + 1)$ **f** $(f - 3)(f - 3)$

Building skills

Savings plans

Toolbox

You can substitute numbers into formulae, these may include negative numbers and decimals.

v^2 is the **subject** of the formula $v^2 = u^2 + 2as$.

Find v when $u = -3$, $a = 9.8$ and $s = 20$.

$$v^2 = u^2 + 2as$$
$$v^2 = (-3)^2 + 2 \times 9.8 \times 20$$
$$v^2 = 9 + 392$$
$$v^2 = 401$$

$$v = +20.02 \text{ or } -20.02 \text{ to 2 d.p.}$$

> Substitute the values given into the formula.

> Square root both sides of the formula to find v.

> Remember that there are two answers when you square root a number, one positive and one negative.

You can **rearrange** a formula to make another letter the subject.

You can use number machines as in Unit 4. A better way is to use a method similar to solving an equation.

You must do the same thing to both sides of the formula to get the variable you want by itself on one side of the formula.

Make s the subject.

$$u^2 + 2as = v^2$$
$-u^2 \qquad \qquad \qquad -u^2$
$$2as = v^2 - u^2$$
$\div 2a \qquad \qquad \qquad \div 2a$
$$s = \frac{v^2 - u^2}{2a}$$

Make u the subject.

$$u^2 + 2as = v^2$$
$-2as \qquad \qquad \qquad -2as$
$$u^2 = v^2 - 2as$$
square root $\qquad$ square root
$$u = \pm\sqrt{v^2 - 2as}$$

Example – Substituting negative numbers into a formula

Work out the value of a when $b = -2$ in this expression

$$a = \frac{3b^2 - 6}{b + 4}$$

Solution

$a = \dfrac{3b^2 - 6}{b + 4}$ ⟵ (Substitute $b = -2$ into the expression.)

$\quad = \dfrac{3 \times (-2)^2 - 6}{(-2) + 4}$ ⟵ (Note that $(-2)^2$ means -2×-2 which is equal to 4.)

$\quad = \dfrac{3 \times 4 - 6}{2}$

$\quad = \dfrac{6}{2} = 3$

Example – Working with formulae

The area of this trapezium is 48 cm².
Work out the height of the trapezium.

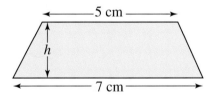

Solution

The formula for the area of a trapezium is

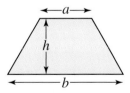

$A = \frac{1}{2} h(a + b)$

So $\quad 48 = \frac{1}{2} h(5 + 7)$ ⟵ (Substitute $A = 48$, $a = 5$ and $b = 7$ into the formula.)

$\frac{1}{2} h(5 + 7) = 48$ ⟵ (It is usual to work with the variable on the LHS of the equation.)

$\quad \frac{1}{2} h \times 12 = 48$

$\quad\quad\quad 6h = 48$

$\quad\quad\quad\; h = 8$

So the height of the trapezium is 8 cm.

Example – Rearranging a formula

The formula for the perimeter of a rectangle is
$$P = 2(l + w)$$

Rearrange the formula to make l the subject.

Solution

Method 1

Look at how Beth and David rearrange the formula:

Beth

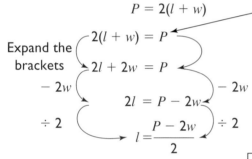

David

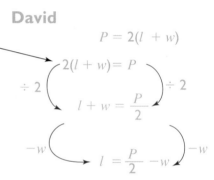

It helps to swap the formula around first.

You must do the same thing to both sides to keep the formula balanced.

Method 2

You can also use a function machine.

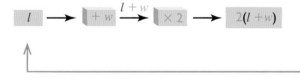

Start with l, the letter that you want to make the subject.

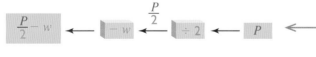

Starting with the original subject of the formula, find the inverse.

So $l = \dfrac{P}{2} - w$

Remember:

✦ Take care with the signs when you substitute negative numbers into a formula: $(-2)^2 = 4$ and $(-2)^3 = -8$.

✦ Take care when you take square roots. The symbol $\sqrt{\ }$ means the positive square root only so $\sqrt{9} = 3$.

✦ When you undo squaring you must take the positive and the negative square root. You can write this as $\pm\sqrt{9} = \pm 3$.

Skills practice A

1 Find the value of $7a + 4b - 3c$ when

  a $a = 2$, $b = 5$ and $c = 3$

  b $a = 6$, $b = -7$ and $c = 2$

  c $a = 0.1$, $b = 0.2$ and $c = 0.3$

  d $a = 0.5$, $b = -0.1$ and $c = 0$.

2 In Rugby Union, the formula to calculate the total score is $S = 5t + 2c + 3g$.

  a What do S, t, c and g stand for?

  b What is the total score when

    i $t = 2$, $c = 1$ and $g = 8$

    ii $t = 10$, $c = 7$ and $g = 12$

  c In one match, England have $t = 2$, $c = 1$, $g = 4$ and Tonga have $t = 3$, $c = 3$, $g = 1$. Who wins?

> **In Rugby Union**
> A try = 5 points
> A conversion = 2 points
> A goal kick = 3 points

3 Find the value of $5x^2 + 3y$ when

  a $x = 2$ and $y = 3$

  b $x = 3$ and $y = 7$

  c $x = 10$ and $y = 30$

  d $x = 5$ and $y = 10$.

4 Find the value of $7h(h + g)$ when

  a $h = 3$ and $g = 2$

  b $h = 5$ and $g = -2$

  c $h = 0$ and $g = 37$

  d $h = 10$ and $g = -3$.

Reasoning

5 Avonford Leisure Centre use this formula to work out the cost, £c, of hiring a badminton court for p people for h hours

$$c = 3h + p$$

  a How much do each of these bookings cost?
   i two people for three hours
   ii four people for two hours
   iii four people for $1\frac{1}{2}$ hours

  b A group of four people pay £10.
   How long do they have the court for?

6 Jenny lets out holiday flats during the summer.
The formula she uses to work out the charge is

   Cost = rate × number of weeks + deposit + £25 per person.

The rate is £275 per week and the deposit is £150.

  a Write out the formula using C to stand for the cost, W for the number of weeks and N for the number of people.

  b Find the cost when
   i four people stay for two weeks
   ii two people stay for three weeks.

  c Three people have £1050 to spend.
   How long can they stay?

7 Use the following formulae.
In each case, give the unit as part of your answer.

  a The perimeter of a rectangle: $P = 2(l + w)$
   Find P, when $l = 10$ and $w = 6$ (in cm).

  b The area of a triangle: $A = \frac{1}{2} bh$.

   Find A, when $b = 20$ and $h = 8$ (in cm).

  c Speed: $v = \dfrac{s}{t}$ Where s is the distance travelled and t is the time taken.

   Find v, when $s = 96\,\text{m}$ and $t = 12$ seconds

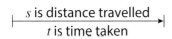

  d The area of a trapezium: $A = \frac{1}{2}(a + b)h$

   Find A, when $a = 10$, $b = 6$ and $h = 5$ (in cm).

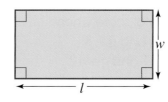

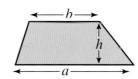

8 The four parts of this question use the four formulae in question **7**.
In each case substitute into the formula to form an equation and then solve the equation.

a A rectangle has a perimeter of 640 cm and length of 200 cm.
Find its width.

b A triangle has an area of 12 cm² and a height of 3 cm.
Find its base.

c A car travels at 40 m s⁻² for 25 seconds.
How far does it go?

d The area of a trapezium is 30 cm².
The parallel sides are 20 cm and 10 cm long.
How far apart are they?

9 Make x the subject in each of these formulae.

a $y = 2x$

b $y = \dfrac{x}{2}$

c $y = x + 3$

d $y = x - 3$

10 Rearrange each of these formulae to make the bold letter the subject of the formula.

a $y = 5 + \boldsymbol{x}$ **b** $y = 5 - \boldsymbol{x}$ **c** $v + \boldsymbol{f} = e + 2$

d $r + \boldsymbol{f} = e + 2$ **e** $a = 3\boldsymbol{b}$ **f** $c = \dfrac{\boldsymbol{d}}{4}$

g $s = u\boldsymbol{t}$ **h** $v = u + a\boldsymbol{t}$ **i** $s = \boldsymbol{q}t - 4$

j $y = 3\boldsymbol{x} + 6$ **k** $x = \boldsymbol{y} + z$ **l** $a = 3\boldsymbol{b} + c$

Skills practice B

1 The formula to convert the temperature in degrees Celsius, C, to degrees Fahrenheit, F, is

$$F = \frac{9C}{5} + 32 \, .$$

a Rewrite these temperature facts using degrees Fahrenheit.

i Water freezes at 0 °C.

ii Water boils at 100 °C.

iii Normal body temperature is 37 °C.

iv The highest recorded temperature in the UK is 38.5 °C.

v The highest recorded temperature in the world is 57.8 °C.

vi The coldest recorded temperature in the UK is –27.2 °C.

vii The coldest recorded temperature in the world is –89.2 °C.

b What is special about –40 °C?

Reasoning

Reasoning

2 Joe, Mary, Ben and Myra are trying to find the value of $5b^2 - 3c$ when $b = 4$ and $c = 2$.
They all get different answers.

No, it's 48.

The answer is 34.

No, it's 74.

You are all wrong! It's 2884.

Joe   Mary   Ben   Myra

Who has the right answer?
Explain where the others have gone wrong.

3 An electrician charges £15 per hour plus a call-out charge of £25.
  a Write a formula for his total charge, £c, for a job lasting h hours.
  b Calculate c when
    i $h = 2$ **ii** $h = 3\frac{1}{2}$
  c Rearrange your formula to make h the subject.
  d Find how many hours he worked when his total charge is
    i £115   **ii** £145   **iii** £77.50.

4 Use the following formulae.
In each case, give the unit as part of your answer.

  a The area of a trapezium: $A = \frac{1}{2}(a + b)h$

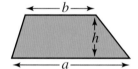

    Find A when $a = 6.4$, $b = 3.2$ and $h = 5$ (in cm).

  b The density, d, of an object of mass m and volume v is given by
    $d = \frac{m}{v}$.
    The air in a 2000 cm³ container has a mass of 2.6 g.
    Find the density of air.

  c The speed of an object, v, is given by
    $v = \frac{s}{t}$.
    Where s is distance travelled and t is time taken.
    A sprinter runs 200 m in 25 seconds.
    Find her speed.

  d The volume of a sphere, $V = \frac{4}{3}\pi r^3$.
    Find V when $r = 6.2035$ cm.

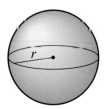

5 The four parts of this question use the four formulae from question **4**.
In each case substitute into the formula to form an equation and then solve it.

  a The area of a trapezium is $25\,\text{cm}^2$.
  The parallel sides are $15\,\text{cm}$ and $10\,\text{cm}$ long.
  How far apart are they?

  b A block of gold of density $19.3\,\text{g}\,\text{cm}^{-3}$ has a volume of $20\,\text{cm}^3$.
  What is its mass?

  c A car travels at $50\,\text{ms}^{-1}$ for 5 minutes.
  How far does it go?

  d The volume of a sphere is $36\pi\,\text{cm}^3$.
  What is its radius?

6 An engineer uses the formula $m = \dfrac{50wh^2}{l}$ to find the mass, in kilograms,
that a beam can support.

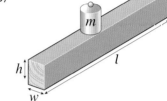

  a Rearrange the formula to make the subject

   i l

   ii w

   iii h.

  b Use the best formula to find the value of

   i m when $l = 300$, $h = 15$ and $w = 20$

   ii l when $m = 800$, $h = 20$ and $w = 18$

   iii w when $m = 640$, $l = 400$ and $h = 16$

   iv h when $w = 20$, $l = 350$ and $m = 700$.

7 Make the bold letter the subject of each of these formulae.

  a $A = 180 - B - \boldsymbol{C}$

  d $S = \boldsymbol{u}t$

  g $m = \dfrac{a + b + c + \boldsymbol{d}}{4}$

  j $A = \boldsymbol{l}^2$

  m $t = \sqrt{\dfrac{\boldsymbol{h}}{5}}$

  b $p = 2(l + \boldsymbol{w})$

  e $c = 2\pi\boldsymbol{r}$

  h $V = \pi r^2 \boldsymbol{h}$

  k $A = \pi \boldsymbol{r}^2$

  n $t = 2\pi\sqrt{\dfrac{\boldsymbol{l}}{g}}$

  c $V = I\boldsymbol{R}$

  f $V = l\boldsymbol{w}h$

  i $A = \frac{1}{2}(a + \boldsymbol{b})h$

  l $x = \sqrt[3]{\boldsymbol{V}}$

  o $h^2 = a^2 + \boldsymbol{b}^2$

8 What do the formulae in question **7** refer to?

Wider skills practice

1 Zoe, Yuri, Xavier and Wan are trying to find the value of $-5e + 3f$ when $e = -4$ and $f = -2$.
Zoe writes -26.
Yuri gets 14.
Xavier's answer is 26.
Wan gets -14.

  a Who is right?

  b Where have the others gone wrong?

Reasoning

2 The volume of a cylinder is given by $V = \pi r^2 h$.

  a What is the volume of a cylinder of height 6 cm and radius 2 cm?

  b Rearrange the formula to make r the subject.

  c Avonford Canning Company makes cylindrical tins for tomato soup.
  Each tin is 11 cm tall and holds 550 cm³ of soup.
  What is the radius of a tin?

3 A Greek mathematician named Hero showed that the area of a triangle, of sides a, b and c could be calculated using this formula.

$$A = \sqrt{s(s - a)(s - b)(s - c)}$$

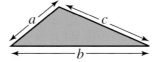

  where $s = \frac{1}{2}(a + b + c)$.

  a Look at these two triangles.
  The side lengths are in centimetres.

  a   **b**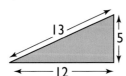

  i Use Pythagoras' theorem to check that they are right-angled.

  ii Use the formula $A = \frac{1}{2}bh$ to find their areas.

  iii Check that Hero's formula gives the same answers.

  b Now use Hero's formula to find the areas of these non-right-angled triangles.

  i $a = 4$ cm, $b = 6$ cm and $c = 8$ cm

  ii $a = 6.7$ cm, $b = 9.3$ cm and $c = 12.9$ cm

4 The paths of the planets round the sun are ellipses, not circles.
The formula for the area of an ellipse is $A = \pi ab$ where a and b are the lengths shown in the diagram.

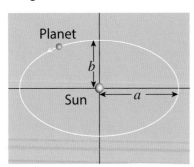

For Pluto, $a = 5.9 \times 10^9$ km and $b = 5.7 \times 10^9$ km.

  a Find the area inside Pluto's orbit.

  b Compare this with the area of a circle of radius 5.8×10^9 km.

Applying skills

Reasoning

1 Morag is investigating isosceles triangles.

She has written this formula connecting the angles.

$b + 2a = 180$

a Write Morag's formula in two other ways.

b Angle a is 50°.
Use one of your formulae to work out angle b.

c One of the angles in an isosceles triangle is 40°.

  i Use your formulae to find what the other angles could be.

  ii Draw the different triangles that you have found.

2 Look at these three dot patterns.

Find a formula for the number of lines, l, joining m red dots to n blue dots.

Hint: Look at the red dots.

How many lines come from each dot?

Reviewing skills

1 Work out the value of y when $x = 0.5$ and when $x = -4$ in these formulae.

  a $y = x^2$ **b** $y = x^3$ **c** $y = 3x^2$

  d $y = (3x)^2$ **e** $y = 2(x^2 - 3)$ **f** $y = \sqrt{1-2x}$

2 The formula for the surface area, S, of a cuboid is $S = 2dw + 2dh + 2hw$.

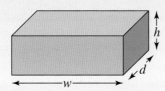

a Work out the surface area of this cuboid.

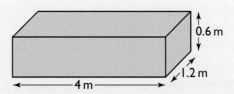

b Work out the height of this cuboid.

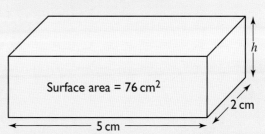

Surface area = 76 cm²

3 Make s the subject of each of these formulae.

 a $a = s + 2$ **b** $b = s - 3$ **c** $c = 5s$

 d $d = \dfrac{s}{4}$ **e** $e = \dfrac{1}{2}s$ **f** $f = \dfrac{3s}{4}$

4 Make x the subject in each of these formulae.

 a $y = 2x + z$ **b** $y = \dfrac{x}{2} - z$ **c** $y = ax + b$

 d $y = \dfrac{x}{a} - b$

5 **a** Write a formula for the area, A_1, of this square.

 b Write a formula for the area, A_2, of this circle.

 c Use your answers to parts **a** and **b** to find a formula for the blue shaded area.

 d In one case, the blue area is $25(4 - \pi)\,\text{cm}^2$.
    Find the value of d.

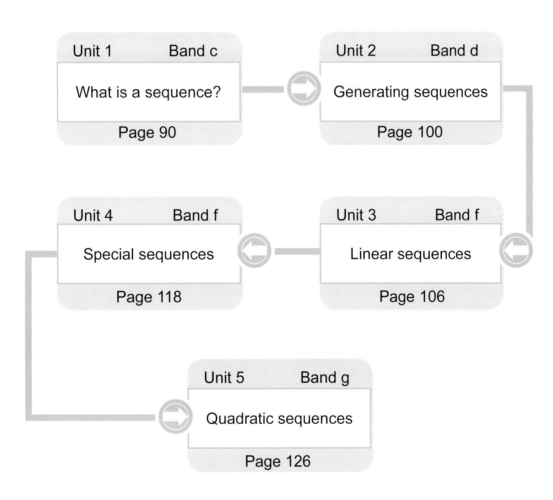

Unit 1	Band c
What is a sequence?	
Page 90	

Unit 2	Band d
Generating sequences	
Page 100	

Unit 4	Band f
Special sequences	
Page 118	

Unit 3	Band f
Linear sequences	
Page 106	

Unit 5	Band g
Quadratic sequences	
Page 126	

Building skills

Preventing fraud

Toolbox

A number **sequence** is a list of numbers that are in order.

There must be a rule to calculate each successive number.

Each number is referred to as a **term** of the sequence.

By finding the rule for moving from one term to another, you can predict the next or missing terms.

In this sequence, the rule is "add 2" to get the next term: 11, 13, 15, 17, 19, … .

In this sequence, the rule is "add 1 to the denominator" to get the next term: $\frac{1}{2}, \frac{1}{3}, \frac{1}{4}, \frac{1}{5} …$

Example – Finding terms of a sequence

Find the missing terms in these sequences.

a 3, 7, 11, ☐, 19, ☐, 27, …

b 3, –3, 3, –3, ☐, ☐, …

c 1, 2, 3, 2, 1, 2, 3, 2, ☐, 2, ☐, …

Solution

a The sequence 3, 7, 11, … has the rule "add 4 to the previous term".

So the missing terms are 15 and 23.

b The rule for the sequence 3, –3, 3, –3, … can be expressed in different ways.

- Change the sign
- Take away 6, then add 6, then take away 6, etc.
- Multiply by –1

Applying one of these rules, the next two terms are 3 and –3.

c The sequence 1, 2, 3, 2, 1, 2, 3, 2, … has a repeating pattern.

1, 2, 3, 2 is repeated so the missing terms are 1 and 3.

Example – Generating sequences from patterns

A farmer has sections of fencing with four bars between each pair of posts.

He puts them together to make a fence.

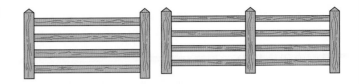

a Draw the next two sections.

b Copy and complete this table.

Number of sections (s)	Number of posts (p)	Number of bars (b)
1	2	4
2	3	
3		
4		

c Use the patterns to work out the number of bars needed for five sections.

Solution

a

b

Number of sections (s)	Number of posts (p)	Number of bars (b)
1	2	4
2	3	8
3	4	12
4	5	16

c Using the rule "add 4", the number of bars is $16 + 4 = 20$.

Remember:

✦ A sequence is an ordered list.

✦ Always work out the rule for moving from one term to another to predict the next or missing terms.

✦ Check your rule works for every term of the sequence.

Skills practice A

1 For each of these sequences, find the differences between the terms.

    a 6, 13, 20, 27, 34, …   **b** 100, 105, 110, 115, 120, …   **c** 2, 3, 5, 8, 12, …

    d 10, 8, 6, 4, 2, …

2 Find the next two terms in these sequences.

    a 7, 10, 13, 16, 19, …   **b** −1, 0, 1, 0, −1, 0, 1, …   **c** 5, 10, 15, 0, 5, 10, …

    d 5, 7, 4, 6, 3, …

3 Match the cards to make sequences.

    There are three cards in each sequence.

1, 2, 3, 4	5, 6, 7, 8
9, 10, 11, 12	38, 35, 32, 29
19, 14, 9, 4	50, 47, 44, 41
38, 45, 52, 59	26, 23, 20, 17
39, 34, 29, 24	66, 73, 80, 87
10, 17, 24, 31	−1, −6, −11, −16

4 For each of these sequences, explain how to find the next term and write down the next three terms.

    a 1, 4, 7, 10, …

    b 28, 24, 20, 16, …

    c 3, 6, 12, 24, …

5 Look at this sequence of triangular matchstick patterns.

    a Draw the next two patterns.

    b Copy and complete this table for the first six patterns.

Number of triangles	1	2	3	4	5	6
Number of matchsticks	3					

    c Predict the number of matchsticks in seven triangles using the patterns in the table.

    d Describe the pattern in the number of matchsticks.

Reasoning

6 Look at this sequence of hexagonal matchstick patterns.

    a Draw the next two patterns.

    b Copy and complete this table for the first six patterns.

Number of hexagons	1	2	3	4	5	6
Number of matchsticks	6					

    c Predict the number of matchsticks in seven hexagons using the patterns in the table.

    d Describe the pattern in the number of matchsticks.

7 Here are the numbers of matchsticks in another sequence of patterns: 5, 9, 13, 17, 21, 25.
Draw some matchstick patterns for this sequence.

8 Copy this spiral onto isometric paper.
Start near the centre of the paper.

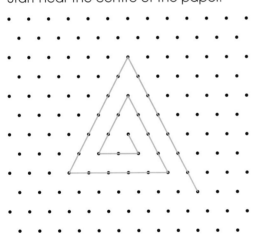

    a Count the number of dots on each line that you draw.
       Write them in a list: 2, 3, 4, … .

    b Predict how many dots will be on the next line.
       Check by drawing and counting.

    c Describe the pattern in the number of dots on the lines in the spiral.

Reasoning

Skills practice B

1 Find the next two terms in these sequences.

    a 2, 4, 6, 8, …   **b** 7, 11, 15, 19, …   **c** 20, 17, 14, 11, …

    d 20, 15, 10, 5, …   **e** 1, 2, 4, 8, …   **f** 1, 4, 9, 16, …

    g 1, 3, 6, 10, …

2 Write down the missing terms in these sequences.

    a 6, 9, ☐, ☐, 18, 21, …   **b** 0, ☐, 16, 24, ☐, 40, …

    c 23, 19, ☐, 11, ☐, 3, …   **d** 1, ☐, ☐, ☐, ☐, 11, …

    e 5, 7, 10, ☐, ☐, 25, …   **f** 3, 5, ☐, ☐, ☐, 13, …

    g 2, ☐, 8, ☐, 14, ☐, …   **h** 21, ☐, 11, ☐, 1, ☐, …

3 Make as many sequences with five terms as you can from these numbers.

    1   3   5   6   10   15

       21   20   25   9   16

    8   2   32   12   4

4 Look at this sequence of square matchstick patterns.

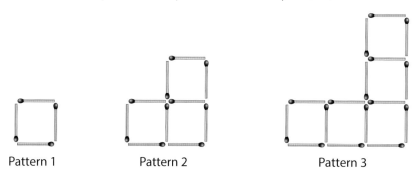

Pattern 1   Pattern 2   Pattern 3

    a Draw the next three patterns.

    b Copy and complete this table for the first six patterns.

Pattern	1	2	3	4	5	6	7	8
Number of squares	1	3						
Number of matchsticks	4	10						

    c Predict how many squares and matchsticks are needed for the next two patterns.

    d Why does the number of matchsticks increase in this way?

5 Look at this sequence of square matchstick patterns.

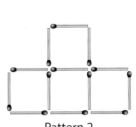
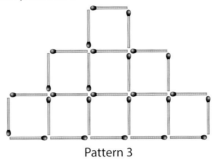

Pattern 1   Pattern 2   Pattern 3

   a Draw the next three patterns.

   b Copy and complete this table for the first six patterns.

Pattern	1	2	3	4	5	6	7	8
Number of squares	1	4						
Number of matchsticks	4	13						

   c Predict how many matchsticks or squares are needed for the next two patterns.

6 Humza writes down the first two numbers in a sequence.

     2, 4, …

Continue the sequence for him.

How many different sequences can you find?

7 Look at this sequence of triangular patterns.

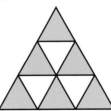

Pattern 1   Pattern 2   Pattern 3

   a Draw the next two patterns.

   b Copy and complete this table.

Pattern	Number of green triangles	Number of white triangles
1		
2		
3		
4		
5		

   c Look at the patterns in the numbers of green and white triangles.
     Write down as many patterns as you can.

   d In pattern 6, how many green triangles are there?
     How many white triangles are there?

   e Draw pattern 6 and check your answers to part **d**.

   f Work out the total number of triangles for pattern 10. (Do not draw it.)

Reasoning

8 Invent your own sequence of patterns using matchsticks and squares.
Show the number of matchsticks and squares in each pattern in a table.

Wider skills practice

Reasoning

1 Meena designs a flow chart.
She tries to make the three times table.

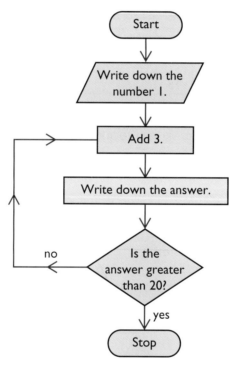

a Copy and complete this table with the numbers made by Meena's flow chart.

Number written down	Is the number greater than 20?
1	No
4	No
22	Yes

*Whoops!
This is not the 3 times table. I have done something wrong!*

Meena

b What does Meena need to change in the flow chart to make the three times table?

2 Ellie drew a circle with the numbers 0 to 9 arranged around the edge.
She used the rule "add 4" to join the numbers.
She wrote down her sequence.

   0, 4, 8, 2, 6, 0, 4, 8, 2, 6, …

Draw a circle like Ellie's with the numbers 0 to 9 around the edge.
Find rules that will join the numbers in these orders.

a 0, 2, 4, 6, 8, 0, …

b 0, 3, 6, 9, 2, 5, 8, 1, 4, 7, 0, …

c 0, 8, 6, 4, 2, 0, …

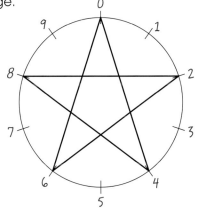

3 Here are three sequences from everyday life.
What do they refer to?
Give the next three terms of each.

a 31, 28, 31, 30, 31, …

b 1, 2, 3, …, 10, 11, 12, 1, 2, …

c 1, 2, 3, …, 58, 59, 60, 1, 2, 3, …

Applying skills

1 Copy this spiral onto squared paper.
Start near the centre of the paper.

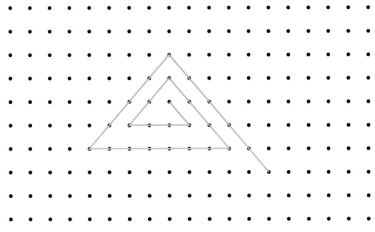

a Count the number of dots on each line that you draw.
Write them in a list: 2, 4, 3, 4, … .

b Predict how many dots are on the next line.
Count them.

c Find the pattern.

Problem solving

2 Sam is using this flow chart.

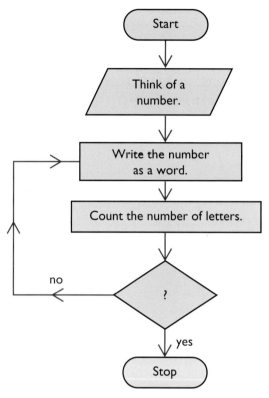

He starts with the number 2 and makes this table.

Start number: 2		
Number of letters	**Number as a word**	**?**
3	THREE	No
5	FIVE	No
4	FOUR	Yes

a What question is needed in the decision box?
b Start chains with different numbers.
   What do you notice?

Reviewing skills

1 Find the missing terms in these sequences.
   a ☐, 8, 16, 32, 64, ☐, …   **b** 4, 1, 4, 1, ☐, ☐, …   **c** 5, 8, 12, ☐, ☐, 30, …

2 Some of these sequences are correct.
   In others, one number is wrong.
   Say which sequences are correct.
   a 6, 10, 14, 18, 22, …   **b** 19, 17, 13, 10, 7, …   **c** 1, 2, 4, 8, 10, …
   d 2, −2, −6, −10, −14, …

3 Look at this sequence of matchstick patterns.

  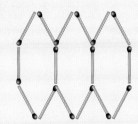

Pattern 1   Pattern 2   Pattern 3

  a Draw the next three patterns.

  b Copy and complete this table for the first six patterns.

Pattern	1	2	3	4	5	6	7	8
Number of matchsticks	6	11						

  c Predict how many matchsticks are needed for the next two patterns.

  d Why does the number of matchsticks increase in this way?

4 Find the first six numbers in these sequences.

  a

  b

Building skills

Example outside the Maths classroom

Code breaking

 ## Toolbox

Sequences can be generated using either **term-to-term rules** or **position-to-term rules**.

- Term-to-term rules are given in the form of instructions such as "add 5".

  If the first term of a sequence is 4, then using the rule "add 5", you could continue the sequence to get 4, 9, 14, 19, ...

  To define a sequence, you must give the term-to-term rule and the first term.

- Position-to-term rules relate each term to its position in the sequence.

  They are formulae.

  The rule "each term is twice its position in the sequence" generates the sequence 2, 4, 6, 8, 10, ...

Position (n)	1	2	3	4
Term	2	4	6	8

The letter n is usually used to represent the position.

This rule can be written as n^{th} term = $2n$.

To calculate any term, for example, the 23rd, substitute the position number, n, into the formula

nth term = 2×23

= 46.

Example – Generating a sequence from a position-to-term rule

Each term of a sequence is generated by the position-to-term rule $2n^2$.

a What are the first five terms?

b What is the 20th term?

Solution

a When $n = 1$, term = $2n^2 = 2 \times 1^2 = 2$. ← Substitute the position number into the formula.

When $n = 2$, term = $2n^2 = 2 \times 2^2 = 8$.

When $n = 3$, term = $2n^2 = 2 \times 3^2 = 18$.

When $n = 4$, term = $2n^2 = 2 \times 4^2 = 32$.

When $n = 5$, term = $2n^2 = 2 \times 5^2 = 50$.

The first five terms of the sequence are 2, 8, 18, 32, 50.

b When $n = 20$, term = $2n^2 = 2 \times 20^2 = 800$.

The 20th term is 800.

Example – Finding and using a position-to-term rule

Find the 100th term of the sequence: 3, 6, 9, 12, 15, ...

Solution

To get from one term to the next, you add three, so the term-to-term rule is "add 3" but it would take some time to reach the 100th term.

Using a table you can see that the term is three times the position number n.

Position (n)	1	2	3	4
Term	3	6	9	12

The position-to-term rule is therefore nth term = $3n$, so the 100th term = $3 \times 100 = 300$.

 Remember:

  ✦ If you give a term-to-term rule, you must also give the first term.
  ✦ n is the position number and appears in a position-to-term formula.

Skills practice A

1 Copy the term-to-term rule and copy and complete each sequence.
The sequence in part **a** has been done for you.

Term-to-term rule   **Sequence**

                                         +3   +3   +3   +3   +3

a Add three   2,   5,   8,   11 , 14 , 17

b Add five   4,   9,   14, ☐ , ☐ , ☐

c Subtract four   20,   16,   12, ☐ , ☐ , ☐

d Add one more each time   2,   3,   5,   ☐ , ☐ , ☐

e Divide by two   16,   8,   4,   ☐ , ☐ , ☐

f Multiply by three   2,   6,   18, ☐ , ☐ , ☐

g Subtract one less each time 50,   41,   33, ☐ , ☐ , ☐

2 For each of these sequences
    i find the next two terms   **ii** give the term-to-term rule.
   Part **a** has been done for you.
   a 2, 4, 8, 16, …
      i Next two terms are: 32, 64
      ii Term-to-term rule is: Multiply by 2

   b 5, 9, 13, 17, …   **c** 81, 27, 9, 3, …   **d** 3, 11, 18, 24, …
   e 42, 36, 30, 24, …   **f** 3, 6, 12, 24, …   **g** 40, 38, 35, 31, …

3 Here are some position-to-term rules.
   i term = 5 × position   **ii** term = position × 3
   iii term = position + 5   **iv** term = position + 3
   Match each of these sequences to the correct position-to-term rule.
   a 3, 6, 9, 12, 15 …   **b** 4, 5, 6, 7, 8 …
   c 6, 7, 8, 9, 10 …   **d** 5, 10, 15, 20, 25 …

4 a Find the missing terms in these sequences.
     i 8, 16, 24, 32, ☐, ☐, 56, …
     ii 11, ☐, 17, 20, ☐, ☐, 29, …
     iii 11, 19, ☐, 35, ☐, ☐, 59, …

   b One of the sequences in part **a** comes from this number machine.

     Which sequence is it?

5 Look at this number machine.

Input → × 4 → − 3 → Output

   a Copy and complete this table for the number machine.
     The first line has been done for you.

Input	Calculation	Output
1	1 × 4 − 3	1
2		
3		
4		
5		

   b What pattern can you see in the output column?
   c Write down the first ten terms of the output sequence.

6 For each of these position-to-term formulae

   a term = position + 7   **b** term = 3 × position

   c term = 5 × position – 2   **d** term = 7 × position + 3

     i draw a number machine

     ii copy and complete this output table

Position	I	2	3	4	5
Term					

     iii give the first term and term-to-term rule.

7 For each of these position-to-term rules

   a term = position + 5   **b** term = 4 × position

   c term = 5 × position   **d** term = 3 × position + 1

     i draw a number machine

     ii find the first five terms of the sequence

     iii describe the patterns you notice in the term-to-term rule.

Skills practice B

1 **a** Find the first five terms for each of these sequences.

     i The first term is 3. To find the next term add 4 to the previous term.

     ii nth term = $n + 1$

     iii The first term is 9. To find the next term subtract 5 from the previous term.

     iv nth term = $2n + 5$

   b Find the 10th term for each of the sequences.

2 **a** Write down the first five terms of the sequences with these position-to-term rules.

     i nth term = $3n$ **ii** nth term = $8n$

     iii nth term = $n + 5$ **iv** nth term = $n + 7$

   b Write down the first number and give the term-to-term rule for each sequence.

3 Write down the term-to-term rule for each of these sequences.

   a 2, 5, 8, 11, 14 …   **b** 3, 7, 11, 15, 19 …   **c** 50, 47, 44, 41, 38 …

   d 9, $10\frac{1}{2}$, 12, $13\frac{1}{2}$, 15 …   **e** 1, 2, 4, 8, 16 …   **f** 1, 10, 100, 1000 …

   g 1, 3, 7, 15 …   **h** 32, 16, 8, 4, 2 …   **i** 2, 6, 18, 54 …

4 Match the sequences on the left with the position-to-term formulae on the right.

4, 8, 12, 16, 20, …		$2n - 6$
2, 3, 4, 5, 6, …		$3n + 2$
−4, −2, 0, 2, 4, …		n^2
5, 8, 11, 14, 17, …		$4n$
1, 4, 9, 16, 25, …		$n + 1$

Reasoning

5 a What do you notice about the term-to-term rules of these sequences?
  i 2, 3, 4, 5, 6, …
  ii 12, 13, 14, 15, 16, …
  iii 102, 103, 104, 105, 106, …
  b Find the position-to-term rules for each of the sequences in part **a**.
  c What do you notice about the position-to-term rules?
  d Find the 100th term of each of the sequences in part **a**.

6 a What is the term-to-term rule in each of these sequences?
  i 3, 5, 7, 9, …   **ii** 4, 7, 10, 13, …
  b Find the 20th term of each sequence.
  c The position-to-term rule for the sequence in part **a i** is given by nth term = $2n + 1$.
    Find the position-to-term rules for these sequences.
  i 4, 6, 8, 10, …   **ii** 2, 4, 6, 8, …   **iii** 2, 5, 8, 11, …
  d Use part **c iii** to help you find the position-to-term rule for the sequence in part **a ii**.

7 A snail is crawling up a tree. The tree is 21 m tall.
  Every day it crawls up 4 m but every night it falls back 2 m.
  a Write down the first six terms in the number sequence that describes the snail's height at the start of each day.
  b How long does it take for the snail to reach the top of the tree?

Wider skills practice

1 For each of the sequences below
  i write down the next three terms.
  ii write down in words the term-to-term rule you are using.

  a 512, 256, 128, 64, …   **b** 2, 5, 8, 11, 14, …   **c** 40, 36, 32, 28, …
  d 1, 4, 9, 16, 25, 36, …   **e** 1, 2, 4, 8, 16, 32, 64, …   **f** −32, −16, −8, −4, …
  g $\frac{1}{2}, \frac{2}{3}, \frac{3}{4}, \frac{4}{5}, \frac{5}{6}, …$

2 For each of the sequences below

    i draw a set of axes taking values of x from 0 to 5 and choosing an appropriate scale for y

    ii plot the sequence as a graph using the position number as the x co-ordinate and the term as the y co-ordinate

    iii describe the shape of the graph.

    a 4, 8, 12, 16, 20, …   **b** 2, 4, 8, 16, 32, …   **c** 30, 25, 20, 15, 10, …

Applying skills

Problem solving

1 Joanne is organising a tombola for her Youth Club.

To win a prize, the number on the ticket must be a term in one of these sequences.

1 nth term $= n^2 + 1$ Chocolates

2 The first term is 1.
The next term is double the previous term.   Cuddly toy

3 The first two terms are both 1.
The next term is the sum of the previous two terms.   CD

4 nth term $= 2n^2 - 1$ Video

Which prizes will these tickets win?

| 17 | 20 | 1 | 9 | 13 | 45 | 50 | 7 | 64 | 36 | 91 | 56 |

Problem solving

2 Which option, A or B, would you rather have?

Option A: £1 a day every day for a month.

Option B: 30p on Monday and then double the amount of the previous day for the rest of the week.

Explain your reasoning.

Reviewing skills

1 Write down the first four terms of these sequences.

    a nth term $= 2n + 1$ **b** nth term $= 3n - 1$

    c nth term $= n^2$ **d** nth term $= n^2 + 1$

2 Find the term-to-term rule for each of these sequences.

    a 1, 7, 13, 19, …   **b** 4, 9, 14, 19, …   **c** 8, 11, 14, 17, …

Building skills Example outside the Maths classroom

Scheduling

Toolbox

The sequence 4, 7, 10, 13, ... is a **linear sequence**.

This is because the gap between successive terms, known as the **difference**, is always the same, in this case 3.

All sequences where the **term-to-term rule** is an addition or subtraction of a constant amount are linear sequences.

The sequence

4, 7, 10, 13 ...

has a constant difference of 3. This means the sequence is linked to the 3 times table.

The position-to-term rule is therefore of the form

nth term = $3n + c$ where c is a number.

The first term will be

1st term = $3 \times 1 + c$

= $3 + c$

So in this case, $c = 1$

Example – Finding the position-to-term formula

For each of the sequences below

i find the next three terms   **ii** find the position-to-term formula

   a 8, 16, 24, 32, 40, ...

   b 27, 25, 23, 21, 19, ...

Solution

a i To get the next term, add 8 each time.

     So the next three terms are 48, 56, 64.

> The difference is 8 so the sequence is related to the 8 times table.

   ii Since the sequence is linear, nth term = $8n$ + a number.

      Look at the first term of the sequence.

      It is 8 so there is no need to add a number in this case.

      So nth term = $8n$.

b i To get the next term, subtract 2 each time.

     So the next three terms are 17, 15, 13.

> The difference is −2 so the sequence is related to the −2 times table.

   ii Since the sequence is linear, nth term = $-2n$ + a number.

      The first term of the sequence is 27.

> $n = 1$ for the first term.

      So nth term = $-2n + 29$.

      Or, more neatly, nth term = $29 - 2n$.

Example – Generating a sequence using a position-to-term rule

Write down the first five terms of the sequence with this position to-term rule.

nth term = $14n + 45$

Solution

Method 1 – using nth term formula for all terms:

When $n = 1$, 1st term = $14 \times 1 + 45 = 59$ ← | **Substitute the term number into the nth term formula.**
When $n = 2$, 2nd term = $14 \times 2 + 45 = 73$
When $n = 3$, 3rd term = $14 \times 3 + 45 = 87$
When $n = 4$, 4th term = $14 \times 4 + 45 = 101$
When $n = 5$, 5th term = $14 \times 5 + 45 = 115$

Method 2 – using position-to-term rule for first term only:

When $n = 1$, 1st term = $14 \times 1 + 45 = 59$
From the formula, the common difference is 14.
2nd term = $59 + 14 = 73$ ← | **Add 14 to previous term.**
3rd term = $73 + 14 = 87$
4th term = $87 + 14 = 101$
5th term = $101 + 14 = 115$

Remember:

✦ In a linear sequence the difference between successive terms is always the same.

Skills practice A

1 For each of these linear sequences, define the sequence by giving the first term and the term-to-term rules.

    a 5, 10, 15, 20, ...   **b** 36, 33, 30, 27, 24, ...   **c** 2, 5, 8, 11, 14, ...

2 For each of these position-to-term rules, write down the first five terms of the sequence.

    a term = 5 × position   **b** term = 3 × position   **c** term = 3 × position + 39

3 The first five terms of a linear sequence are 60, ☐, ☐, 51 and 48.

    a Find the values of the missing terms.

    b The 100th term is –237.

       What is the 101st term?

4 Find the first five terms of each of these sequences.

    a The first term of the sequence is $-\frac{3}{4}$.

       To find the next term add $\frac{1}{2}$ to the previous term.

    b $n \rightarrow 4 - 2n$.

5 Match these number machines with the correct table.

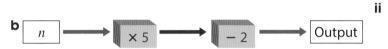

a $n \longrightarrow \times 3 \longrightarrow + 4 \longrightarrow$ Output

i

Input, n	1	2	3	4	5
Output	0	5	10	15	20

b $n \longrightarrow \times 5 \longrightarrow - 2 \longrightarrow$ Output

ii

Input, n	1	2	3	4	5
Output	7	10	13	16	19

c $n \longrightarrow + 3 \longrightarrow \times 2 \longrightarrow$ Output

iii

Input, n	1	2	3	4	5
Output	8	10	12	14	16

d $n \longrightarrow - 1 \longrightarrow \times 5 \longrightarrow$ Output

iv

Input, n	1	2	3	4	5
Output	3	8	13	18	23

6 For each of these number machines, copy and complete the table and then write down the rule in the form output = ☐.

a Input, n → $+ 9$ → Output

Input, n		2	7		15
Output	10			19	

b Input, n → $\times 4$ → Output

Input, n	1		7	9	
Output		16			44

c Input, n → $\times 3$ → $+ 3$ → Output

Input, n	1		5		
Output		12		30	39

d Input, n → $\times 6$ → $- 5$ → Output

Input, n	3				12
Output		25	37	61	

7 a Draw a number machine for each of these rules.

  i output = $n + 7$ **ii** output = $8n$ **iii** output = $4n + 4$

b Use inverse number machines to find which term in the sequences generated by these rules has a value of 64.

8 Look at this rule.

> The first term is a. To find the next term, add d to the term before.
>
> For example in the sequence 3, 7, 11, 15, 19, ..., $a = 3$ and $d = 4$.

Write down the values of a and d for each of these sequences.

  a 2, 5, 8, 11, 14, ...   **b** 5, 10, 15, 20, 25, ...   **c** 17, 19, 21, 23, 25, ...

  d 9, 7, 5, 3, 1, ...   **e** 45, 41, 37, 33, 29, ...   **f** 8, 4, 0, ...

9 a Find the 6th term of each of these sequences.

  i 5, 7, 9, 11, ...   **ii** 6, 9, 12, 15, ...   **iii** 1, 5, 9, 13, ...

b Write down the first four terms of the sequences with these position-to-term rules.

  i nth term = $3n + 4$ **ii** nth term = $2n - 1$ **iii** nth term = $n - 3$

c What connections are there between parts **a** and **b**?

d Use your observations from part **c** to find the position-to-term rule for these sequences.

  i 2, 4, 6, 8, ...   **ii** 3, 6, 9, 12, ...   **iii** 3, 5, 7, 9, ...   **iv** 2, 5, 8, 11, 14, ...

Reasoning

10 Quentin has a large number of tables.
Each one is an equilateral triangle.
He sets them out in long lines.

 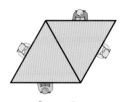 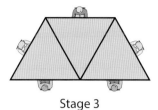

Stage 1   Stage 2   Stage 3

a Draw stages 4 and 5.

b Copy and complete this table.

Number of tables	1	2	3	4	5
Number of seats	3				

c How many people can sit at
i 10 tables   **ii** 20 tables?

11 Alison is making a sequence of patterns out of matchsticks.

Pattern 1   Pattern 2   Pattern 3

a Draw the next two patterns.

b Copy and complete this table.

Pattern	1	2	3	4	5
Number of matchsticks					

c How many matchsticks are being added each time?

d How many matchsticks are needed for
i the 6th pattern   **ii** the 10th pattern   **iii** the 100th pattern?

e Work out the position-to-term formula.

Skills practice B

1 Use the position-to-term rules to work out the 1st, 2nd, 5th, 8th and 12th terms of each sequence.
Explain why each is a linear sequence.

a nth term $= 3n + 5$ **b** nth term $= n + 5$ **c** nth term $= 6n$

d nth term $= 4n + 7$ **e** nth term $= 5n - 3$

2 For the sequence $n + 10$

a find the first term and the term-to-term rule.

b find the 50th term.

Reasoning

Reasoning

3 Write out these position-to-term rules using the correct algebraic notation.
The first has been done for you.

  a The nth term is found by doing $2 \times n + 3$.   nth term = 2n + 3

  b The nth term is found by doing $n \times 3 + 2$.

  c The nth term is found by doing $5 \times n - 1$.

  d The nth term is found by doubling n and adding 10.

  e The nth term is found by adding 5 to 6 times n.

4 Denise thinks of the sequence 7, 9, 11, 13, ...

  a What are the next three terms of the sequence?

  b Find the nth term of the sequence.

  c Use your formula to find the 50th term.

  d Which term has a value of 27?

5 The first seven terms of a sequence are: 6, ☐, ☐, 18, ☐, ☐, 30.

  a Find the term-to-term rule.

  b Find the missing terms of the sequence.

  c Find a position-to-term rule for this sequence.

  d What is the 50th term?

6 Joe is building four footpaths at a crossroads in the local park.
He needs to know how many paving stones he will need.

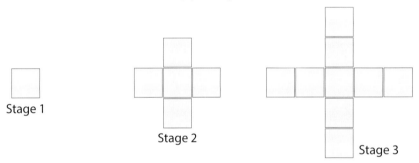

Stage 1

Stage 2

Stage 3

  a Draw the next three stages.

  b Copy and complete this table.

Stage	1	2	3	4	5	6
Number of paving stones	1	5				

  c Predict how many paving stones Joe will need for stage 10.

  d What pattern do you notice?
Write down the nth term rule in words.

7 a Write down the next two terms of the sequence 50, 45, 40, 35... .

  b The nth term of this sequence is $55 - 5n$.

  i Explain where the $-5n$ comes from.

  ii Explain where the 55 comes from.

  c Which term in this sequence has the value of 0?

  d Which term in this sequence has the value of 20?

Reasoning

8 For each of these sequences

    i find the formula for the nth term

    ii work out the 80th term.

  a 8, 12, 16, 20, ...   **b** 19, 21, 23, 25, ...

  c 300, 306, 312, 318, ...   **d** 10, 15, 20, 25, ...

9 Here are three nth term formulae.

    nth term = $7n + 14$

    nth term = $7n - 14$

    nth term = $5n + 14$

  a Write down the first five terms of each sequence.

  b What is the same and different about the sequences?

  c Which term in each of these sequences has a value of 84?

10 For each of these sequences

    i find a formula for the nth term

    ii work out the 40th term:

  a 200, 198, 196, 194, ...   **b** 60, 53, 46, 39, ...

  c 71, 70, 69, 68, ...   **d** 82, 85, 88, 91, ...

11 Look at this sequence of patterns. They are made out of triangular tiles.

  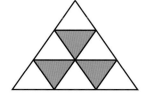

Pattern 1   Pattern 2   Pattern 3

  a Draw the next pattern.

  b Copy and complete this table.

Pattern	1	2	3	4
Number of tiles				

  c How many triangular tiles are added each time?

  d Is this a linear sequence?

Reasoning

12 Penny is making a sequence of patterns using hoops.

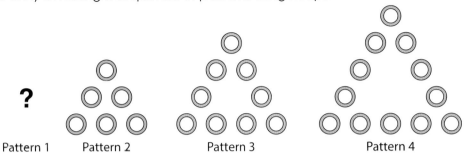

Pattern 1   Pattern 2   Pattern 3   Pattern 4

   a Draw pattern 1.
   b Draw patterns 5 and 6.
   c Copy and complete this table for the first six patterns.

Pattern	1	2	3	4	5	6
Number of hoops		6				

   d How many hoops are needed for
      i pattern 7   **ii** pattern 10   **iii** pattern 20?
   e Explain how you worked out your answers to part **d**.

13 This is a sequence of patterns with red and blue tiles.

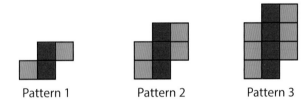

   Pattern 1   Pattern 2   Pattern 3

   a Draw pattern 4.
   b Copy and complete this table.

Pattern	1	2	3	4	10	20
Number of red tiles	2	3				
Number of blue tiles	2	4				

   c Think about pattern n.
      Write down expressions for the number of
      i red tiles   **ii** blue tiles   **iii** tiles in total.
      Give your answers as simply as possible.

Wider skills practice

1 Look at these chairs.

a Copy and complete this table.

Number of chairs	1	2	3	4	5	6
Number of legs	4					

b Copy these axes.
Plot the values from the table as points on the graph. The point (1, 4) will represent 1 chair with 4 legs.

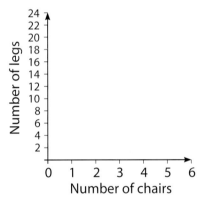

c What do you notice about your points?

d Is the sequence of the number of legs linear?

2 This number machine is used to generate a sequence

Use the numbers 1, 2, 3, …, up to 10 as the input.
Write down the output sequence.
Explain what has happened.

3 a For each of these sequences, write down the next three terms and how you found them.

    i $\frac{1}{2}$, 1, 2, 4   **ii** 35, 30, 25, 20   **iii** 5.0, 4.8, 4.6, 4.4

    iv 0.1, 1, 10, 100   **v** 3.5, 4, 4.5, 5, 5.5

b Which of the sequences in part **a** are not linear sequences?

Reasoning

4 Here is part of a spreadsheet.
Each column is a different sequence.

	A	B	C	D	E	F	G
1	1	7	7	7	7	7	7
2	2	11	14	13	5	10	8
3	3	15	21	19	3	13	9
4	4	19	28	25	1	16	10
5	5	23	35	31	−1	19	11
6	6	27	42	37	−3	22	12

The numbers in the columns B to G are formed from Column A.
These are the formulae used to generate the sequences.

a

=A1+6
=A2+6
=A3+6
=A4+6
=A5+6
=A6+6

b

=A1+7
=A2+7
=A3+7
=A4+7
=A5+7
=A6+7

c

=A1*4+3
=A2*4+3
=A3*4+3
=A4*4+3
=A5*4+3
=A6*4+3

d

=A1*6+1
=A2*6+1
=A3*6+1
=A4*6+1
=A5*6+1
=A6*6+1

e

=A1*3+4
=A2*3+4
=A3*3+4
=A4*3+4
=A5*3+4
=A6*3+4

f

= 9 −A1*2
= 9 −A2*2
= 9 −A3*2
= 9 −A4*2
= 9 −A5*2
= 9 −A6*2

Which formulae are used to generate each of the columns?

5 The table gives the time taken to roast a joint of meat.

Mass (m) of meat in kilograms	1	2	3	4	5
Time (t) in minutes	30	40	50	60	70

a Find a formula for the roasting time in terms of the mass of the meat.

b How long will it take to roast a joint of meat with a mass of 8.5 kg?

6 Sarah is building a fence.
These are the first two sections.

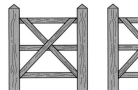
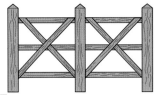

   a Draw the next three sections.

   b Copy and complete this table.

Section number	1	2	3	4	5
Number of diagonal bars	2				
Number of horizontal bars	3				

   c How many diagonal bars and horizontal bars are needed for the 10th section?

   d Write down the rules you used to make your predictions.

7 Alex is laying a straight garden path using regular octagonal paving stones.
Each side is 1 foot long.

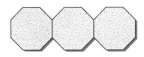

Stage 1   Stage 2   Stage 3

   a Draw the next three stages.

   b Make a table showing the perimeter of the first six stages.

   c How do you find the perimeter of the next stage?

   d Predict the perimeter of a path with 20 paving stones.

Applying skills

1 **a** Use your calculator to multiply 142 857 by the first seven integers in turn. Copy this table and use it to record your results.

×	142 857
1	142 857
2	
3	
4	
5	
6	
7	

   b What do you notice about your answers so far?

   c Use your calculator to complete the next two rows of your table.

   d Investigate your table for number patterns and complete the next five rows of your table without using a calculator.

   e Check your results.

   f Now use your calculator to work out: $\frac{1}{7}, \frac{2}{7}, \frac{3}{7}, \dots$

   g What do you notice about your results?

Problem solving

2 Mark is investigating L-shapes on this 5 × 5 grid.
Here are two of his shapes.

1	2	3	4	5
6	7	8	9	10
11	12	13	14	15
16	17	18	19	20
21	22	23	24	25

This is L_1.

This is L_4.

L-shape	working out	Total
L_1	$1 + 6 + 11 + 12$	30
L_2		
L_3		
L_4	$4 + 9 + 14 + 15$	42
L_6		
L_{14}		

a Copy and complete the table.

b Why is there no L_5?

c What patterns or rules do you notice?

d Investigate L-shapes on

   i a 6 × 6 grid   **ii** a 7 × 7 grid   **iii** an 8 × 8 grid.

e Investigate these two shapes on different-sized grids.

3 Here is a piece of string.
With one cut you get two pieces.

a How many pieces do you get with two cuts?

b What about three cuts and four cuts?

   Copy this table and use it to record your results.

Number of cuts (c)	0	1	2	3	4	5	6	7	8
Number of pieces (p)	1	2							

c What is the rule relating the number of cuts to the number of pieces of string?

d How many pieces of string will you get with 50 cuts?

e For each of these experiments, draw a table of results, look for the pattern and find the rule for the values of p.

   i Fold a piece of string once and make different
      numbers of cuts.

   ii Fold a piece of string twice and make different
       numbers of cuts.

   iii What happens when you fold a piece of string three,
        four or five times and then make one cut?

f Put all your rules into a table.

g Describe the pattern in your rules.

Reviewing skills

1 Maria is using number cards to make sequences.

   a Where could she place the remaining cards so that each line is a sequence?

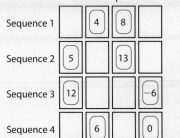

   You can use each card once only.

   b Write down the term-to-term rule for each of the sequences you make.

   c Which sequences are linear?

2 **a** Write down the term-to-term rule, including the first term, for the sequences with these nth terms.

      i $2n + 1$ **ii** $4n - 3$ **iii** $5n - 6$

   b How do you know these sequences are linear?

3 **i** Find the values of the missing terms of these linear sequences.

   ii Write down the position-to-term formula for each.

   a 16, ☐, ☐, 22, ☐, 26, ...   **b** 50, ☐, ☐, 35, ☐, 25, ☐, ...

   c −20, ☐, −16, −14, ☐, ☐, ...

4 Find the first term and the constant difference for these sequences.

   a 4, 8, 12, 16, ...   **b** Multiples of 3   **c** 100, 95, 90, 85, ...

   d −10, −8, −6, −4, ...   **e** Multiples of 5   **f** Even numbers

5 Avonford High School's canteen uses trapezium-shaped tables.
Each table can seat seven people.
The tables are laid out in long lines.

   a Draw the next two stages.

   b Copy and complete this table.

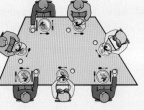

Stage 1

Number of tables	1	2	3	4	5
Number of seats	7	12			

   c Predict how many people can sit at

      i six tables   **ii** eight tables

   d Find the formula for n tables.

   e How many people can sit at a line of 20 tables?

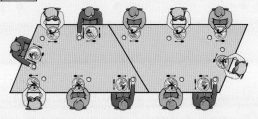

Stage 2

Building skills

Example outside the Maths classroom

Patterns in nature

 Toolbox

There are some important number sequences that are not linear (i.e. that do not have a constant difference between terms).

- **The triangular numbers:** 1, 3, 6, 10, ... (that is, 1, 1 + 2, 1 + 2 + 3, 1 + 2 + 3 + 4, etc.).

    The difference between successive terms increases by one each time.

    The position-to-term formula for the triangular numbers is nth term = $\dfrac{n(n + 1)}{2}$.

- The **square numbers**: 1, 4, 9, 16, 25, ... (that is 1 × 1, 2 × 2, 3 × 3, 4 × 4, 5 × 5, etc.).

    The difference between successive terms is 1, 3, 5, 7, 9, etc. and the position-to-term formula is nth term = n^2.

- The **Fibonacci numbers**: 1, 1, 2, 3, 5, 8, 13, 21, ... where each term (after the initial two) is the sum of the two previous terms.

    The difference between successive terms is the Fibonacci sequence itself!

Many sequences are variations of these.
For example,

    101, 104, 109, 116 is the sequence of square numbers plus 100
    3, 12, 27, 48 is the sequence of square numbers multiplied by 3.

Example – Investigating triangular numbers

Look at this sequence of patterns.

Triangle 1   Triangle 2   Triangle 3

a Draw the next three triangles.

b How many dots are there in each triangle?

c What pattern do you notice in the number sequence?

d The formula for the nth term of the sequence is $\dfrac{n(n + 1)}{2}$.

    Use this formula to check your answer for triangle 5.

e Find the 10th triangular number.

Solution

a

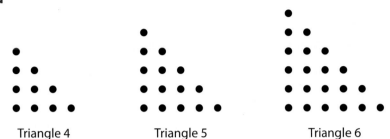

Triangle 4   Triangle 5   Triangle 6

b Triangle 1 has 1 dot.
Triangle 2 has 3 dots – 2 dots are added.
Triangle 3 has 6 dots – 3 dots are added.
Triangle 4 has 10 dots – 4 dots are added.
Triangle 5 has 15 dots – 5 dots are added.
Triangle 6 has 21 dots – 6 dots are added.

c The number of dots added increases by one each time.

d For $n = 5$,

$$\frac{n(n + 1)}{2} = \frac{5 \times 6}{2} = 15$$

> Substitute $n = 5$ into the formula.

So the answer for triangle 5 is right.

e When $n = 10$,

$$= \frac{n(n + 1)}{2}$$

$$= \frac{10 \times 11}{2}$$

$$= 55$$

 Remember:

✦ When the difference between successive terms increases by one each time, the sequence is related to triangular numbers.
✦ When the difference between successive terms is consecutive odd numbers, the sequence is related to square numbers.

Skills practice A

1 What is the rule for this sequence: 1, 4, 9, 16, 25, 36, 49, 64, 81, 100?

2 Robin and Shomeet collect pebbles from the beach.
When they get home they play a game.
They take it in turns to add pebbles to make this sequence of patterns.

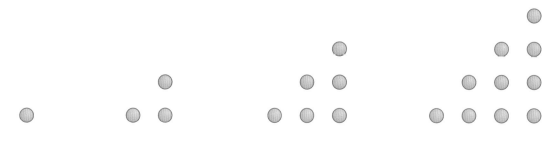

Robin   Shomeet   Robin   Shomeet

  a Write down the number of pebbles in each of the patterns.

  b How many pebbles are there in each of the next three patterns?

  c What is the special name given to this sequence?

  d Write down the formula for the nth term of the sequence.

  e Find the number of pebbles in

    i the 10th pattern

    ii the 20th pattern

    iii the 50th pattern

Skills practice B

1 **a** Write down the first four terms of the sequences produced by these formulae.

    i nth term $= n^2 + 5$

    ii nth term $= n^2 - 2$.

  b Which number is in both sequences?

2 Joe is investigating triangular numbers.

  a Why do you think they are called triangular numbers?

  b What are the first six triangular numbers?
    Draw their triangles.

  c Joe puts two of his triangles together to make a square.
    Which other triangular numbers can be used to make a square number?

6 + 10 = 16

Reasoning

3 You can put two triangles with the same number of dots together to make a rectangular pattern.

Rectangle 1   Rectangle 2   Rectangle 3

a For each of the rectangles above state
  i the length
  ii the width
  iii the number of dots.

b Predict the length and width of
  i the 10th rectangle
  ii the 20th rectangle
  iii the 100th rectangle.

c Predict the number of dots in
  i the 10th rectangle
  ii the 20th rectangle
  iii the 100th rectangle.

d For the nth rectangle, give expressions for
  i the length
  ii the width
  iii the number of dots.

e Use your answers to part **d** to show that the formula for the nth triangular number is $\frac{1}{2}n(n + 1)$.

4 Here are the first five terms of the Fibonacci sequence.

  1, 1, 2, 3, 5, …

a Write out the sequence until the terms get bigger than 1000.
b Describe the pattern of odd numbers and even numbers.
c Identify the terms that are multiples of 3.
d What do you notice about their term numbers?
e What about the terms that are multiples of 5?

5 Pascal was a French mathematician born in 1623.
He used a special triangle for some of his work on calculation.
Here are the first three rows of Pascal's triangle.

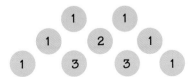

> Each number is the sum of the two numbers just above it.

a Copy them and add the next two rows.
b Draw a line under any diagonal that contains the counting numbers.
c Draw a loop around any diagonal that contains the triangular numbers.

Wider skills practice

1 Look at these dot patterns.

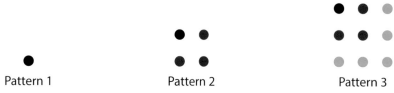

Pattern 1   Pattern 2   Pattern 3

a Draw the next two patterns.

b Copy and complete this table.

Pattern	2	3	4	5	6	7
Number of dots added to previous pattern	3	5				

c What type of number are the terms of this sequence?

d How many dots are added to the 9th pattern to make the 10th pattern?

e How many dots are there in each of the first seven patterns?
  What type of number are these?

f How many dots are there in
  i the 10th pattern
  ii the 20th pattern
  iii the 100th pattern?

g What is the sum of the numbers 1 + 3 + 5 + 7 + 9 + 11 + 13 + 15?
  What pattern number has this number of dots?

h What is the sum of the first
  i 3 odd numbers
  ii 4 odd numbers
  iii 5 odd numbers
  iv 10 odd numbers
  v 20 odd numbers
  vi 100 odd numbers?

i Write an expression for the sum of the first n odd numbers.

2 In a sequence you start by writing down a two-digit number, say 14.
The next term is the sum of the squares of the last two digits of the previous term.
For example,

  14, $1^2 + 4^2 = 17$, $1^2 + 7^2 = 50$, $5^2 + 0^2 = 25$,   …
  Term 1   Term 2   Term 3   Term 4

a Find the first five terms of the sequence with this rule whose first term is 25.

b Find the 2001st term of the sequence with this rule whose first term is 25.

Reasoning

Reasoning

3 Use a spreadsheet to complete this question.

a Copy the table and extend it to show the first 25 Fibonacci numbers.

What do you notice about the division column?

Term number	Fibonacci number	Division
F_1	1	
F_2	1	1 ÷ 1 = 1 ←
F_3	2	2 ÷ 1 = 2 ←
F_4	3	3 ÷ 2 = 1.5

$F_2 ÷ F_1$

$F_3 ÷ F_2$

b Write down another Fibonacci-type sequence by starting with any two numbers other than 1, 1.
Repeat part **a**.

4 Look at this sequence of rectangles.
They are made up of squares.

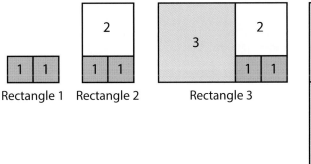

Rectangle 1   Rectangle 2   Rectangle 3

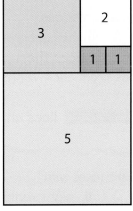

Rectangle 4

a Continue the sequence for the next two rectangles.

b Look at the numbers in the rectangles.
Write the numbers in rectangle 6 in order, smallest first.
What do you notice?

c How can you work out the sequence without drawing rectangles and squares?

Applying skills

1 Look at this pattern. It is called a mystic rose.

It has five vertices.

Each vertex is joined to every other vertex by a straight line.

Count the straight lines; you should get 10.

a Copy and complete this table.

Number of vertices	Number of straight lines
1	0
2	1
3	
4	
5	10
6	

b Copy and complete these sentences.

In a mystic rose with n vertices there are
_____ lines from each vertex.

So there are _____ lines altogether.

c Test your formula for mystic roses with

   i seven vertices   **ii** eight vertices   **iii** ten vertices.

2 The term-to-term rule for a sequence is "take the previous term, divide by 3 and then add 4".
The first term is 1.

  a Show that the second term of the sequence is $4\frac{1}{3}$ (or 4.3).

  b Find the third and fourth terms.

  c What happens eventually?

  d Investigate with different values for the first term.

  e Show that $n = 6$ is the solution to the equation $n = \frac{n}{3} + 4$.

  f Explain where this equation comes from.

  g Investigate what happens when you use other numbers in the rule, for example divide by 5 and then add 8.

3 If everyone in the class shook hands with everyone else how many handshakes would there be?
Start by imagining that there are only two people in the class, then three, and so on.

Reviewing skills

1 Sequence A is the triangular numbers.

Sequence B is the triangular numbers but starting with 0:

0, 1, 3, 6, … .

a Write down the first six terms of each sequence.

b Add the first terms of sequences A and B together to make the first term of a new sequence C. Repeat to form the first six terms of sequence C.

c Describe sequence C.

d Draw patterns of dots to explain your answer to part c.

2 Look at this sequence of patterns.

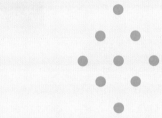

Pattern 1   Pattern 2   Pattern 3

a Draw the next two patterns.

b Copy and complete this table.

Pattern	1	2	3	4	5
Number of dots	1	3			

c Find a formula for the number of dots in the nth pattern.

Building skills

Building bridges

Toolbox

The sequence of **square numbers** begins 1, 4, 9, 16, 25, ...

The differences between these terms are 3, 5, 7, 9, ... and the difference between these differences is constant. In this case, it is 2.

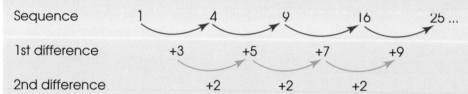

Sequence	1	4	9	16	25 ...
1st difference	+3	+5	+7	+9	
2nd difference	+2	+2	+2		

Such sequences are known as **quadratic sequences** and the expression for the nth term always contain a term in n^2.

For example, the formula for the nth term of a simple quadratic sequence rule might be $n^2 + 1$, which would give 2, 5, 10, 17, 26, ...

To find the rule for a quadratic sequence, look at the relationship between the square numbers (1, 4, 9, 16, 25) and the sequence itself.

Example – Generating terms of a quadratic sequence

Find the fourth and sixth terms of the sequence whose nth term is given by $3n^2 - 8$.

Solution

When $n = 4$,

$$3n^2 - 8 = 3 \times 4^2 - 8$$
$$= 3 \times 16 - 8 \quad \longleftarrow \boxed{\textbf{Squaring first.}}$$
$$= 48 - 8 \quad \longleftarrow \boxed{\textbf{Then multiplication.}}$$
$$= 40$$

When $n = 6$,

$$3n^2 - 8 = 3 \times 6^2 - 8 \quad \longleftarrow \boxed{\textbf{Substitute 6 into the formula.}}$$
$$- 3 \times 36 - 8 \quad \longleftarrow \boxed{\textbf{Squaring first.}}$$
$$= 108 - 8 \quad \longleftarrow \boxed{\textbf{Then multiplication.}}$$
$$= 100$$

Example – Finding the *n*th term of a quadratic sequence

Here is a sequence of patterns.

  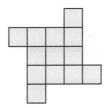

Pattern 1   Pattern 2   Pattern 3

a Draw pattern 4.

b The number of squares in each pattern forms a sequence.
What are the first five terms of the sequence?

c Find the *n*th term of this sequence.
Explain how the patterns help you to find the *n*th term of the sequence.

Solution

a

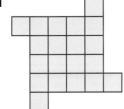

Pattern 4

b From the diagrams, the first four terms are 5, 8, 13, 20.

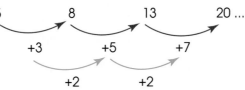

Sequence   5   8   13   20 ...

1st difference   +3   +5   +7

2nd difference   +2   +2

The next first difference will be 9, so the fifth term is 29.

c The first differences are not the same so the sequence is not linear.
The second differences are the same so this is a quadratic sequence.

Square numbers   1   4   9   16   25   ⟵   **Start with the square numbers.**

                 +4   +4   +4   +4   +4

This sequence   5   8   13   20   29   ⟵   **To get the required sequence, add 4.**

The *n*th term is therefore $n^2 + 4$.

Look at the pattern.

• The first pattern is a 1 × 1 square plus four single squares.
• The second pattern is a 2 × 2 square plus four single squares.
• The third pattern is a 3 × 3 square plus four single squares.

So the *n*th pattern will be an *n* × *n* square plus four single squares, giving $n^2 + 4$ squares in total.

> **Remember:**
>
> ✦ A quadratic sequence is related to the sequence of square numbers.
> ✦ You may find it easier to find the formula for the nth term by examining the patterns that produced the sequence.

Skills practice A

1 Write down the first five terms of the sequences given by these rules.

    a nth term = $n^2 + 5$ **b** nth term = $n^2 - 3$ **c** nth term = $3n^2$

    d nth term = $2n^2 + 4$ **e** nth term = $4n^2 - 3$ **f** nth term = $2n^2 + n$

2 Match the sequences **a** to **e** with the rules **i** to **v**.

    a   3, 12, 27, 48, ...   **i** nth term = $20 - 4n$

    b   99, 96, 91, 84, ...   **ii** nth term = $5n - 1$

    c   16, 12, 8, 4, ...   **iii** nth term = $n^2 + 2$

    d   4, 9, 14, 19, ...   **iv** nth term = $3n^2$

    e   3, 6, 11, 18, ...   **v** nth term = $100 - n^2$

3   **a**   Find the missing term in each of these sequences.

         i   1, 4, 9, ⬚, 25, ...

         ii   2, 5, 10, ⬚, 26, ...

         iii   2, 8, 18, ⬚, 50, ...

         iv   5, 11, 21, ⬚, 53, ...

         v   6, 13, 24, ⬚, 58, ...

    b   Find the rule for the nth term for each of the sequences in part **a**.

4   **a**   Use a table like the one below to find the first 12 terms and the first, second and third differences of each of these sequences.

        The first one is started for you.

        i nth term = n^2

Term	n^2	1st difference	2nd difference	3rd difference
1	1			
2	4	3		
3	9	5	2	
4	16	7	2	0
5	25	9	2	0

        ii nth term = $n^2 + 1$

        iii nth term = $n^2 + 2$

    b   What can you say about the first and second differences of linear and of quadratic sequences?

Skills practice B

1 a Use a table like the one bellow to find the first 12 terms and the first, second and third differences of each of these sequences.

The first one is started for you.

You may use a spreadsheet.

i nth term = $n^2 + 7$

Term	$n^2 + 7$	1st difference	2nd difference	3rd difference
1	8			
2	11	3		
3	16	5	2	
4	23	7	2	0
5	32	9	2	0

ii nth term = $n^2 - 3$ **iii** nth term = $5n^2$

iv nth term = $2n^2 + 5$ **v** nth term = $200 - 3n^2$

vi nth term = $n^2 + 50n$ **vii** nth term = $n^2 + n + 3$

viii nth term = $n^2 + 3n - 11$

b Mary says that a quadratic sequence always has a constant second difference. Is she right?

2 Match the sequences **a** to **f** with the formulae for the nth terms **i** to **vi**.

  a 4, 16, 36, 64, 100, ...   **i** nth term = $n^2 + 7$

  b 98, 92, 82, 68, 50, ...   **ii** nth term = $4n^2$

  c 8, 11, 16, 23, 32, ...   **iii** nth term = $30 - n^2$

  d 3, 8, 15, 24, 35, ...   **iv** nth term = $2n^2 - 5$

  e 29, 26, 21, 14, 5, ...   **v** nth term = $n^2 + 2n$

  f −3, 3, 13, 27, 45, ...   **vi** nth term = $100 - 2n^2$

3 a Which of these sequences are quadratic?

  i 4, 7, 12, 19, 28, ...   **ii** 0, 3, 8, 15, 24, 35, ...

  iii 2, 6, 11, 17, 27, ...   **iv** 2, 8, 18, 32, 50, 72, ...

  v 3, 12, 26, 47, 74, ...   **vi** 3, 9, 19, 33, 51, 73, ...

b For the quadratic sequences, compare the sequence to the square numbers and find the formula for the nth term.

Reasoning

Wider skills practice

1 A ball is thrown into the air.

Its height is recorded every second.

The table shows the sequence of heights.

Time, t (seconds)	0	1	2	3	4	5	6	7
Height, h (metres)	0	30	50	60	60	50	30	0

  a Use a table to find the first and second differences.

  b Explain how this tells you that the sequence is quadratic.

  c The formula for the sequence is $h = 35t - kt^2$ where k is a number.
    Find the value of k.

2 Joe is building four footpaths at a crossroads in the local park and filling the corner areas by laying turf.

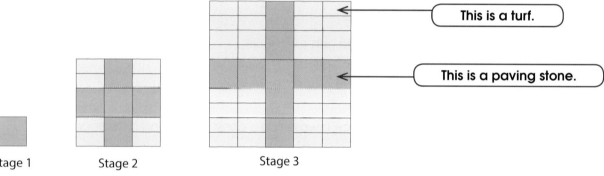

This is a turf.

This is a paving stone.

Stage 1   Stage 2   Stage 3

  a Draw the next three stages.

  b Copy and complete this table.

Stage number	1	2	3	4	5	6
Number of paving stones	1	5				
Number of turfs	0	8				

  c Predict how many paving stones and turfs Joe will need for stage 10.

  d What patterns do you notice?
    Write down the rules in words and using the letters s, p and t.

3 Mr Jones is a gardener.

He makes a table showing the lengths of square lawns and the cost of putting lawn food on them.

Length of lawn (metres)	1	2	3	4	5	6	7
Cost of lawn food (pence)	15	45	95	165	255	265	495

The formula for the nth term of this sequence is $10n^2 + k$.

  a Find the value of k.

  b What is the cost of lawn food for a square lawn of side 8 metres?

  c Mrs Bell's lawn food costs £8.15.
    What size is her square lawn?

Reasoning

4 Fibonacci's famous sequence is 1, 1, 2, 3, 5, 8, 13, 21, ...

    a How does the sequence work?

    b What are the values of the next two terms?

    c Put the sequence in a table and make columns for the first and second differences.
       Complete the table.

    d Look carefully at the first and second difference columns.
       What do you notice?

    e Is the Fibonacci sequence linear, quadratic or neither?

Applying skills

Problem solving

1 Scott is designing a new park for Avonford.
He has several different plans.
Here are two.

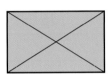

> There is an entrance to the park at each vertex.

Scott has made the plans so that there is a path from each entrance to every other entrance.

    a There are two diagonal paths crossing the park in the rectangular plan.
       How many diagonals are there in the pentagon?

    b Scott wants to find the number of diagonals for a 9-sided shape.
       He makes a table to help him solve the problem.
       Copy and complete the table.

Number of sides	4	5	6	7
Number of diagonals	2			

    c What pattern do you notice?

    d Predict how many diagonals are needed for a nonagon (which has nine sides).

    e What formula should Scott use to find the number of diagonals in an *n*-sided polygon?

2 Look at this 4 by 4 jigsaw puzzle.

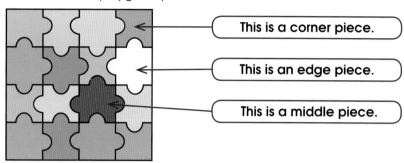

This is a corner piece.

This is an edge piece.

This is a middle piece.

a Copy and complete this table.

Jigsaw size, n by n	Number of corner pieces, c	Number of edge pieces, e	Number of middle pieces, m	Total number of pieces, t
2 by 2				
3 by 3				
4 by 4	4	8	4	16
5 by 5				
10 by 10				

b Find formulae for c, e, m and t for an n by n jigsaw.

c Use your formulae to show that $c + e + m = t$ for an n by n jigsaw.

d Investigate rectangular jigsaw puzzles.
Start by finding a rule for
i 2 by n jigsaws　　**ii** 3 by n jigsaws　　**iii** 4 by n jigsaws.

3 a This tower has three levels and is made from 15 playing cards.
Investigate for different numbers of levels.
At one time the world record for a tower had 61 levels.
i How many cards are needed for 61 levels?
ii Would it fit in an ordinary room? A typical playing card is 9 cm × 6 cm.

b How high was the tower with 61 levels?

Reviewing skills

1 Write down the first four terms of each of these sequences.
　a nth term = $n^2 + 1$　　**b** nth term = $n^2 + 3$　　**c** nth term = $n^2 + n$
　d nth term = $n^2 + 2n$　　**e** nth term = $n^2 - n + 1$

2 For each of these sequences
　　i find the next three terms
　　ii find the nth term.
　a 5, 8, 13, 20, 29, ...　　**b** 0, 3, 8, 15, 24, ...　　**c** 3, 12, 27, 48, 75, ...
　d 7, 10, 15, 22, 31, ...

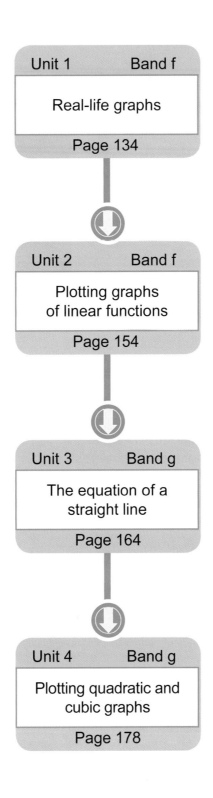

Unit 1   Band f

Real-life graphs

Page 134

Unit 2   Band f

Plotting graphs
of linear functions

Page 154

Unit 3   Band g

The equation of a
straight line

Page 164

Unit 4   Band g

Plotting quadratic and
cubic graphs

Page 178

Building skills

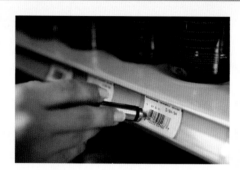

Example outside the Maths classroom

Setting prices

Toolbox

Graphs are diagrams used to represent data.

They show the relationship between (usually) two things, such as time and distance.

They consist of one or more straight lines or can be curved, depending on the situation.

Data is usually easier to interpret on a graph than in a table.

There are some crucial pieces of information you must use to read the story that a graph tells.

- The title explains what the story is about.
- The labels on the axes tell you what the points represent.
- The shape of the graph tells you how the relationship changes.

Reading graphs sometimes allows you to make predictions about what will happen in any given circumstance.

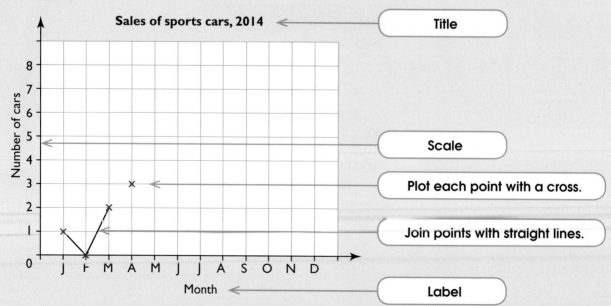

Example – Reading distance–time graphs

Look at this graph showing the height of a hot air balloon.
It is called a travel graph or a distance–time graph.

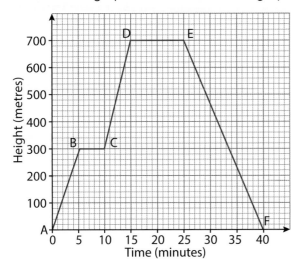

a How high does the balloon go?

b What is shown by the lines BC and DE?

c For how long is the balloon at a height of 300 m?

d How long does the balloon take to land?

e When is the balloon at a height of 500 m?

Solution

a The balloon reaches a maximum height of 700 m.

> The maximum height is the largest value of y that the graph reaches.

b The lines BC and DE represent times when the balloon remains at the same height.

> The lines BC and DE are horizontal lines.

c The balloon is at 300 m for 5 minutes.

> Given by the length of line BC.

d It takes 15 minutes to come down.

> The line EF begins 25 minutes into the flight and finishes at 40 minutes.

e It is at a height of 500 m at $12\frac{1}{2}$ minutes on the way up and at 29 minutes on the way down.

> Draw a line horizontally from 500 m on the y axis and read off the x value of the point where it crosses the graph.

Example – Understanding the shape of graphs

The diagram shows the shape of Jane's bath.

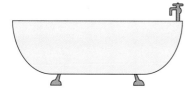

Water runs in at a constant rate.

Which sketch graph best shows the relationship between the depth of the water and time?

Justify your answer.

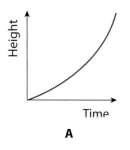

A

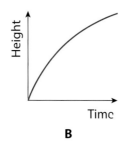

B

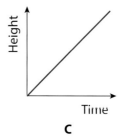

C

Solution

Graph **B** is correct.

Initially the cross-section of the bath is small and the bath fills up more quickly.

As time elapses the cross-sectional area increases thus slowing down the rate of increase in depth.

Remember:

✦ A horizontal line on a distance–time graph means the object is stationary.

✦ Steeper lines on a distance-time graph mean greater speed.

✦ Sloping lines do *not* represent objects going uphill!

Skills practice A

1 Jamila plants an apple tree. The graph shows its growth.

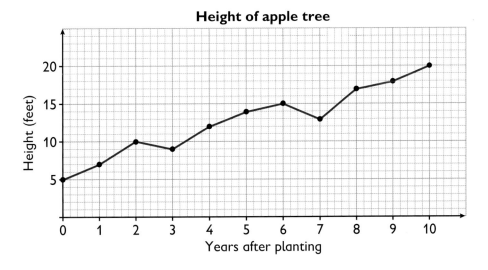

Height of apple tree

a How high is the tree when Jamila plants it?

b How high is it after 5 years?

c When is it 17 feet high?

d In which years does Jamila prune it?

e In which year does it grow the most?

Reasoning

Reasoning

2 Mark walks to his local shop to buy some fruit and then returns home.

Here is a distance–time graph for his journey.

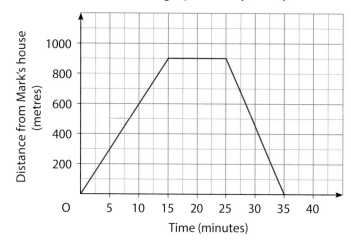

a What does the shape of the graph tell you about Mark's journey?

b How far is the shop from Mark's home?

c How long does Mark spend in the shop?

d How long does it take Mark to walk home?

3 Sam goes to the post office.
- The post office is 800 m from his home.
- It takes Sam 10 minutes to get there.
- Sam spends 5 minutes in the post office.
- He sets off to return home.
- He covers the first 400 m in 10 minutes.
- He then has a rest for 5 minutes.
- The final 400 m home takes him 15 minutes.

The first stage of Sam's journey is shown below.

Copy the diagram and draw lines to show the rest of his journey.

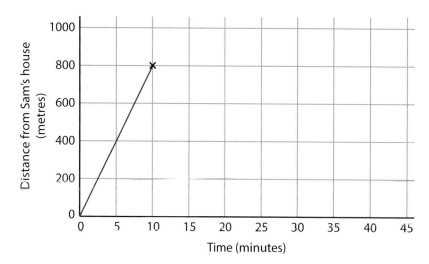

4 These graphs show the temperature for four different days.
Match the descriptions **a** to **d** to the graphs **i** to **iv**.

a The temperature stays cool all day.

b The temperature starts cool, warms up and then cools down.

c The temperature starts warm and then cools down.

d The temperature goes up and down a lot.

i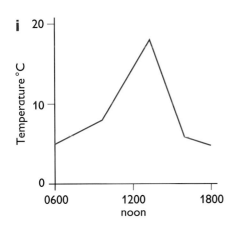

ii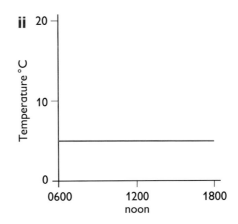

iii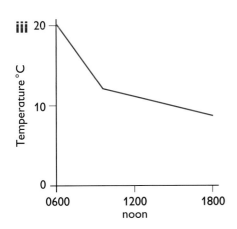

iv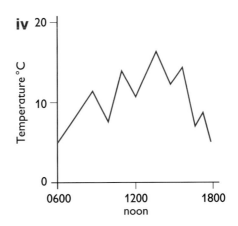

5 The graph shows the income tax paid on different salaries in a certain country.

a Annette's salary is £9000.
How much tax does she pay?

b Sam's salary is £22 000.
Estimate how much tax he pays.

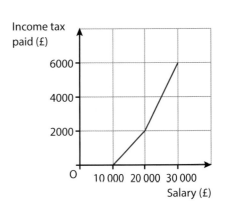

6 The table shows the hourly temperature at Palma on a particular day.

Time	9 a.m.	10 a.m.	11 a.m.	12 noon	1 p.m.	2 p.m.	3 p.m.	4 p.m.
Temperature (°C)	10	15	29	30	35	33	30	28

    a Show this information as a smooth curve on a graph.

    b Between which times does the temperature rise most quickly?

    c Between which times does the temperature fall most rapidly?

    d Estimate for how long the temperature exceeds 29 °C.

7 Thena took part in her local half-marathon.

    The graph shows the number of spectators at the finishing point during the day.

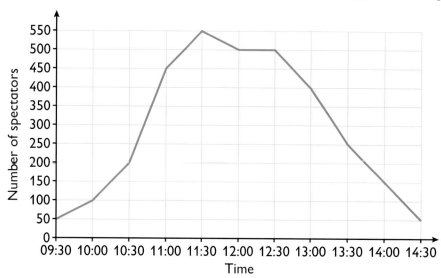

    a What is the largest number of spectators?

    b When is the crowd the largest?

    c How many spectators are there at 2 p.m.?

    d How big is the crowd when Thena finishes at 12.45 p.m.?

8 Richard collects rain water in a tank.

    He records the level in the tank on the first day of each month.

Date	1 Jan	1 Feb	1 March	1 April	1 May	1 June	1 July	1 Aug	1 Sept	1 Oct	1 Nov	1 Dec
Level of water in tank (mm)	800	760	770	910	715	715	795	580	440	1030	940	885

    a Plot the data points on a graph and join them with straight lines.

    b When is there least water in the tank?

    c In which month is there no change?

    d **i** In which month is the greatest change?

      ii Was this the wettest month?

Skills practice B

1 Each of these situations can be represented by a graph.

a Match the situations **i** to **v** with the graphs **A** to **E**.

i The temperature, y, of a cup of coffee left to cool in a room, plotted against time, x.

ii The number of litres of fuel, y, left in the tank of a car moving at constant speed, plotted against time, x.

iii The distance, y, travelled by an accelerating racing car, plotted against time, x.

iv The number of harmful bacteria, y, left in the body as it responds to treatment, slowly at first then more rapidly, plotted against time, x.

v The number of dollars, y, you can buy for a number of pounds sterling, x.

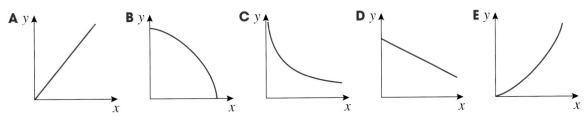

b Describe in words graphs **A** to **E**.

c All these graphs use x and y.

Suggest other suitable letters for each one.

2 P, Q and R are three consecutive stations on a railway line.

The travel graph shows the journey of a train from P to R via Q.

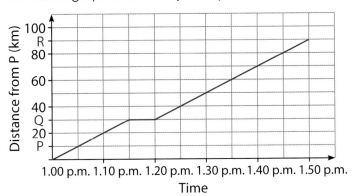

a **i** When does the train arrive at Q?

ii For how long does the train stop at Q?

iii What is the average speed of the train between P and Q?

iv What is the distance between stations Q and R?

b A second train leaves R at 1:15 p.m.

It travels non-stop to Q, arriving at 1:45 p.m.

i Copy the travel graph and show the second train's journey on it.

ii When do the two trains pass each other?

iii How far apart are the trains at 1:40 p.m.?

3 Normal body temperature is 37 °C.

A patient's body temperature is measured every hour. The table shows the readings.

Temp (°C)	37.6	37.8	37.9	37.9	38.0	38.0	38.0	37.8	37.3	37.1	37.0	37.0	37.0
Time	8 a.m.	9 a.m.	10 a.m.	11 a.m.	12 noon	1 p.m.	2 p.m.	3 p.m.	4 p.m.	5 p.m.	6 p.m.	7 p.m.	8 p.m.

a Draw a line graph to show these data.

b What is the highest temperature?

c For how long does the patient have their highest temperature?

d When is the patient's temperature 37.9 °C?

e When does the patient reach normal temperature?

f When does the patient start to recover?

g When is the greatest temperature change?

4 Becky walks from Bridgetown to Avonford.

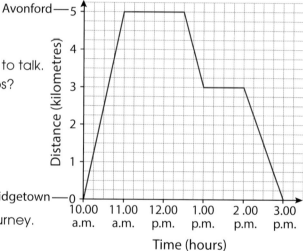

a When does Becky leave Bridgetown?

b How long does she spend in Avonford?

c On the way back Becky sees a friend. She stops to talk. How far is Becky from Bridgetown when she stops?

d How long does she stop for?

e Dorje is a long-distance runner.
He runs from Bridgetown to Avonford.
He leaves at 1 p.m. and arrives at 1.30 p.m.
How far does he run?

f Copy Becky's graph on to graph paper.
Add a line to your graph representing Dorje's journey.

g At what time does Dorje pass Becky?
What is Becky doing at that time?

h How far is Dorje from Avonford when he passes Becky?

5 The graph shows the height of a basketball plotted against the time after throwing.

a What happens to the ball in the first two seconds?

b Give a reason for the shape of the graph when *t* is greater than 3.

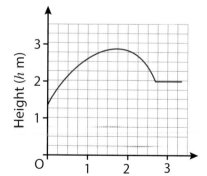

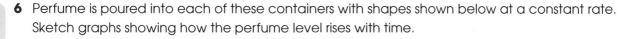

6 Perfume is poured into each of these containers with shapes shown below at a constant rate.
Sketch graphs showing how the perfume level rises with time.

a   **b**   **c**   **d**

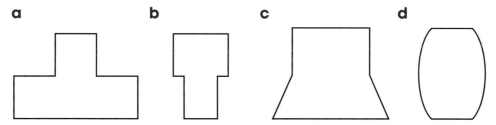

7 The table shows the depth of water in a harbour during one day.

Time of day	09:00	10:00	11:00	12:00	13:00	14:00	15:00	16:00	17:00	18:00	19:00	20:00	21:00
Depth (metres)	1.00	1.27	2.00	3.00	4.00	4.73	5.00	4.73	4.00	3.00	2.00	1.27	1.00

a Show this information as a smooth curve.
   Use 1 cm for one hour and 2 cm for one metre.
b Estimate the depth of water at 11:30.
c A ship requires a depth of at least 2.5 m of water to enter the harbour.
   Between which times is it safe for the ship to enter?

8 Davis car hire company charges for the number of kilometres travelled.
The table shows the charge for certain distances.

Distance (km)	0	50	100	150	200	250	300
Hire charge (£)	0	15	30	45	55	65	75

a Draw axes from 0 km to 300 km on the horizontal axis and £0 to £75 on the vertical axis.
   Plot a graph to illustrate the information in the table.
b Describe how the hire charge changes as you travel greater distances.
c Use your graph to find how much you pay when you travel
   i 75 km
   ii 280 km
d Use your graph to find how far you have travelled when the hire charge is
   i £70
   ii £48
e The charges of a second car hire firm, U Drive, are shown in this table.

Distance (km)	0	50	100	150	200	250	300
Hire charge (£)	10	20	30	40	50	60	70

   On the same axes plot a graph to show U Drive's charges.
f For what distance do the two companies charge the same amount?

9 Draw a sketch graph to describe each of the following situations.

a From rest you start running until you reach flat-out speed.
Then you slow down gradually until you collapse from exhaustion. Your distance, s, is plotted against time, t.

b The temperature in degrees Celsius, C, of the water in a kettle
when it is heated to boiling, plotted against time, t.

c The number of bacteria left in the body, y, as an infection responds to treatment, slowly at first, then more rapidly, plotted against time, t.

Wider skills practice

1 Ann travels to school.

- She walks 0.3 km from home to the bus stop in 4 minutes.
- She then waits 2 minutes for the bus.
- The bus travels 1.2 km in 5 minutes to a bus stop near the school.
- Ann walks the last 0.2 km to school in 4 minutes.

a Draw a horizontal axis from 0 minutes to 16 minutes using a scale of 1 cm to represent 1 minute.
Draw a vertical axis from 0 km to 2 km using a scale of 1 cm to represent 0.1 km.
Plot a travel graph to illustrate Ann's journey to school.

b What is the average speed of the bus in metres per minute?

c Convert this speed to kilometres per hour.

2 Angela, Bob and Cathy leave Deetown and travel in the same direction.

- Angela sets off at 11:30 a.m. and travels 48 km by car.
  It takes her $1\frac{1}{2}$ hours.
- Bob leaves at 10:30 a.m., walks 4 km in an hour and then catches a bus which travels another 13 km.
  The bus journey takes 1 hour.
- Cathy cycles, setting off at 11 a.m.
  She travels 28 km in 2 hours.

a Draw axes from 10 a.m. to 2 p.m. on the horizontal axis and from 0 km to 50 km on the vertical axis.
Plot the travel graphs for all three people.

b At what time does Angela pass Bob?

c At what time does Angela pass Cathy?

d At what times does Cathy pass Bob?

e At what speed is Angela driving?

f At what speed is Cathy cycling?

3 Tandeep and Ruth are studying changes of state in their chemistry lesson.
They heat some solid paraffin wax in a test tube until it melts.
Then they measure its temperature every 2 minutes as it cools and solidifies.
The table shows their results.

Time (minutes)	Temperature (°C)	Time (minutes)	Temperature (°C)
0	86	26	45
2	70	28	41
4	62	30	37
6	57	32	33
8	55	34	30
10	55	36	28
12	55	38	26
14	55	40	24
16	55	42	23
18	55	44	22
20	55	46	22
22	53	48	22
24	50	50	22

a Plot these points on a graph, with time in minutes on the x axis and temperature in °C from 0 to 90 on the y axis.
Join the points with a smooth curve.
This graph is the cooling curve for paraffin wax.

b What is the temperature of the paraffin wax after

i 5 minutes

ii 27 minutes?

c How long does it take the wax to cool from its initial temperature to 65 °C?

d When a liquid cools to its melting point, the temperature stays the same until it has all become solid.
What is the melting point of paraffin wax?

e What is room temperature?

f Tandeep and Ruth repeat the experiment with a different wax.
This wax has a melting point of 64 °C.
Starting from the same initial temperature sketch a cooling curve for this wax.

4 Look at the line graph in this newspaper article.

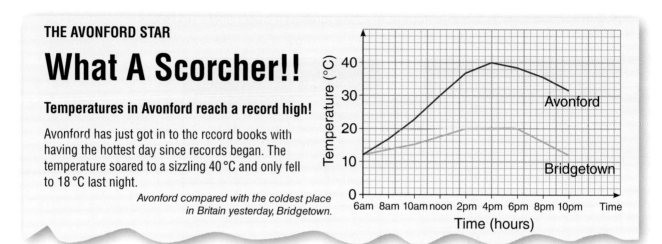

THE AVONFORD STAR

What A Scorcher!!

Temperatures in Avonford reach a record high!

Avonford has just got in to the record books with having the hottest day since records began. The temperature soared to a sizzling 40 °C and only fell to 18 °C last night.

Avonford compared with the coldest place in Britain yesterday, Bridgetown.

a What is the temperature in both towns at 11 o'clock?

b At which times is the temperature in Bridgetown 18 °C?

c This is a conversion graph.
You can use it to convert between Fahrenheit and Celsius temperatures.

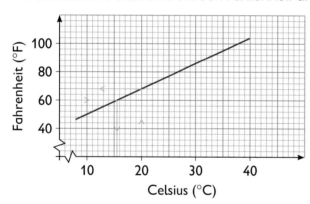

Write down the temperature in each town for every hour.
Use the conversion graph to convert the temperatures to Fahrenheit.

d Make your own newspaper article and line graphs using the Fahrenheit temperatures.

e Comment on the shape of your line graphs compared with the line graphs in the newspaper article.

f Can you convert exactly between Celsius and Fahrenheit by using the conversion graph?

5 Katie is talking to her mother.

One cat year is the same as 7 human years, Katie.

But, Mum, Tiger is 20.

Katie does not believe her mother.
She gets this graph from the vet.

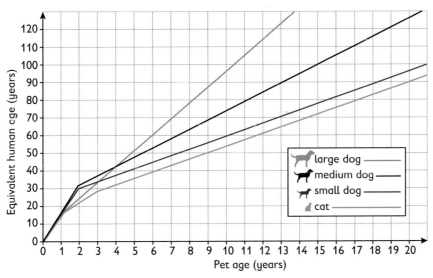

a What is Tiger's age in human years?

b Which is older, in human years, a 10-year-old large dog or a 19-year-old cat?

c Is it ever true that a dog's human age is seven times its real age?

d Is it ever true that a cat's human age is seven times its real age?

e Look at the gradients of the lines on this graph.
   What do they tell you?

6 The faster you drive, the more space you need to stop.
The Highway Code gives this information about stopping distances.

Typical stopping distances

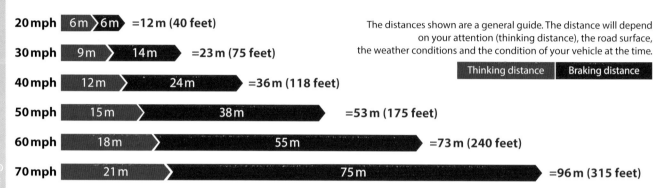

20 mph 6m 6m =12 m (40 feet)

30 mph 9m 14m =23 m (75 feet)

40 mph 12m 24m =36 m (118 feet)

50 mph 15m 38m =53 m (175 feet)

60 mph 18m 55m =73 m (240 feet)

70 mph 21m 75m =96 m (315 feet)

The distances shown are a general guide. The distance will depend on your attention (thinking distance), the road surface, the weather conditions and the condition of your vehicle at the time.

| Thinking distance | Braking distance |

a Bruce is driving at 45 miles an hour (mph) and Brenda is driving at 65 mph.
What are their stopping distances?

b Draw a graph of stopping distances.
Use the horizontal axis for the speed, going up to 80 mph (scale: 1 cm to 10 mph).
Use the vertical axis for the distance, going up to 500 feet (scale: 1 cm to 50 feet).
Plot the six points from the Highway Code and join them with a smooth curve.

c Use your graph to check your answers to part **a**.

d What is the stopping distance for 52 mph?

e What is the stopping distance for 15 mph?
(You will need to extend your curve.)

f You are driving 200 feet behind Bruce.
What is your maximum safe speed?

g Do you think the curve should go through (0, 0)?
Explain your answer.

Reasoning

Reasoning

7 Janine has made an electrical heater for a plant propagator.
She tests it in a container of damp soil and plots the data on a graph.

Time (minutes)	0	1	2	3	4	5	6	7	8
Temperature (to nearest °C)	17	21	23	25	22	26	27	27	27

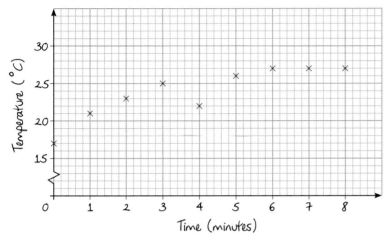

a Janine thinks one of her readings is wrong.
   Which one is this?
b What should she do about it?
c How should she join the data points?

Applying skills

Problem solving

1 Think about your journey to school.
   a Describe your journey.
   b Draw a travel graph of your journey.
   c Make up two questions for a friend to answer about your travel graph.

Problem solving

2 The table shows the value of £100 left in a savings account for eight years.

Time (years)	0	1	2	3	4	5	6	7	8
Value of investment (£)	100	110	121	133	146	161	177	194	214

a Plot these points on a graph.
   Join them with a smooth curve.
b How much is the investment worth after $2\frac{1}{2}$ years?
c After how long is the investment worth double its original value?

3 A bus is travelling at 10 metres per second towards a bus stop 50 metres away.

Here is a possible distance-time graph.

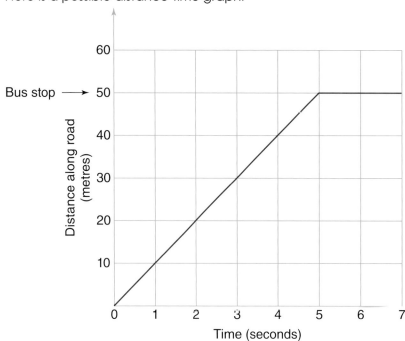

During the first 5 seconds, the bus is travelling at a constant speed of 10 m/s.

Then, on arrival at the bus stop, it suddenly stops dead in its tracks!

This is shown by the way in which the graph makes a sudden turn.

a What would happen if a real bus behaved in this manner?

b In the real world, a bus begins to slow down before it reaches the bus stop, and gradually comes to a halt.

This is represented using smooth curves.

Redraw the graph to show what that might look like.

c Use your graph to find

i when the driver begins to brake

ii when the bus actually stops

iii for how long the bus decelerates (slows down).

4 For each of the situations below, sketch a distance–time graph which will describe the events shown.

a

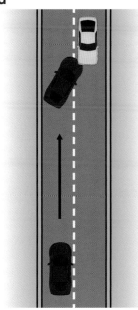

b

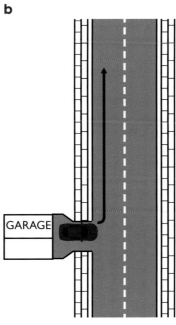

c

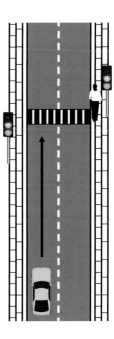

d

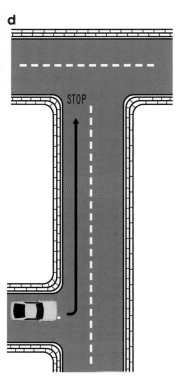

e

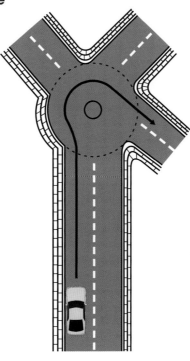

f

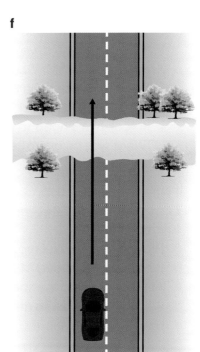

Reviewing skills

1 The graph represents Mr Watson's journey from London to Stockport.

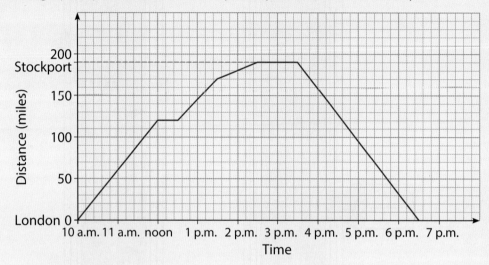

a Mr Watson stopped for a break at a service station.
  I When did he stop?
  ii For how long did he stop?
b He met heavy traffic on one part of the trip.
  i How long was this for?
  ii How far did he drive under these conditions?
c At what time did Mr Watson arrive in Stockport?
d For how long was he in Stockport?
e i How far is it from Stockport to London?
  ii It took him 3 hours to drive home.
    What was his average speed?

2 A ferry leaves Aveley at 9 a.m. and sails 100 kilometres to Bornley.
It arrives there at 2 p.m.

At 10:30 a.m. a speedboat leaves Aveley and travels at 40 km/h to Bornley.

a Draw a single travel graph to describe these journeys.
b What was the speed of the ferry?
c At what time did the speedboat arrive at Bornley?
d When did the vessels meet?
e How far apart were the vessels at 11 a.m.?

3 The graph shows the price of Oldcastle United plc shares at the close of business each week day (Monday to Friday) over a 10-day period.

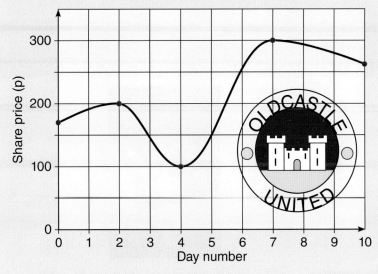

The share price halved between the 2nd and 4th days.

Peter

a What is the difference between the initial and final share prices?

b During which periods was the share price increasing?

c When was the best time to buy shares?

d When was the best time to sell shares?

e Is Peter's statement true or false?

4 The graph shows the height of perfume in a bottle varying with time when the bottle is filled at a constant rate.

Which of these shapes is the correct shape of the bottle?

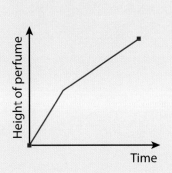

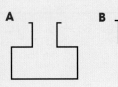

Building skills

Scientific research

Toolbox

Functions can be represented on a mapping diagram.

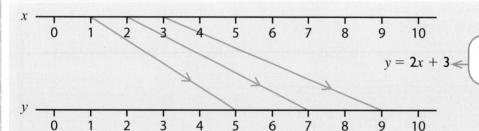

$y = 2x + 3$

> This is sometimes written $x \rightarrow 2x + 3$

Every value on the x line maps to a corresponding value on the y line.

Inverse mappings return you to where you started.

Another way to represent a function is to plot its graph.

> Join the plotted points together.

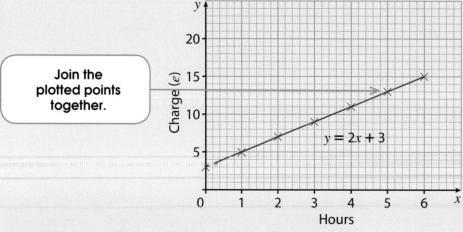

A linear function is represented by a straight line graph.

Conversion graphs are an example of linear functions.

Start by drawing a table of values.

This table is for the function $y = 2x + 3$.

x	1	2	3	4	5	6
$2x$	2	4	6	8	10	12
$+ 3$	3	3	3	3	3	3
$y = 2x + 3$	5	7	9	11	13	15

Example – Drawing and using a mapping diagram

1 For the function $x \rightarrow x + 3$:

   a make a table of values with x from 0 to 6.

   b draw a mapping diagram.

   c write down the value of y when $x = 4$

   d find the value of x when $y = 5$.

Solution

a

x	0	1	2	3	4	5	6
$+3$	3	3	3	3	3	3	3
$y = x + 3$	3	4	5	6	7	8	9

b

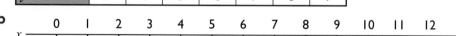

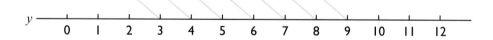

c When $x = 4$, $y = 7$. ⟵   You can find this value from your table or from your mapping diagram.

d When $y = 5$, $x = 2$. ⟵   Using the mapping diagram in reverse shows that $y = 5$ comes from $x = 2$.

Example – Drawing and using a graph of a linear function

In a science experiment, the length of a piece of elastic is recorded when different masses are hung on it.
Here are the results.

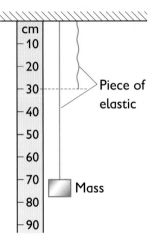

Mass, x grams	0	10	20	30	40
Length of elastic, y cm	30	40	50	60	70

a Plot the graph.

b Find the mass that stretched the elastic to 56 cm.

Solution

a

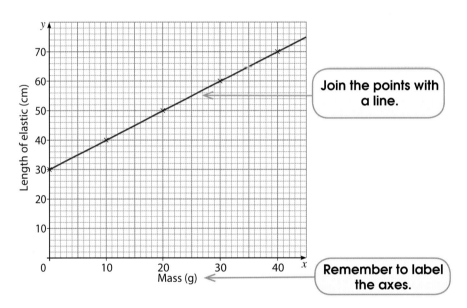

Join the points with a line.

Remember to label the axes.

b The mass would have been 26 g. Draw a horizontal line from 56 cm on the vertical axis. Read off the x value of the point where this line meets the graph line.

Remember:

✦ A linear function has a straight-line graph.
✦ Make a table of values before you draw the graph of a function.

Skills practice A

1 a Draw the mapping diagram for this table of values.

x	0	1	2	3	4	5
y	1	2.5	4	5.5	7	8.5

b Draw a graph to represent this mapping.

c How can you tell from the graph that y is a linear function of x?

2 Look at this mapping diagram.

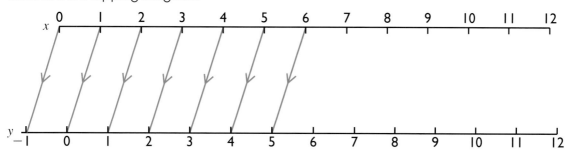

a Copy and complete this table of values.

x	0	1	2			
y	−1					

b Draw the graph of y against x.

c Write down the equation of the function.

3 Look at this sign.

PICK YOUR OWN STRAWBERRIES JUST **£2** per kilogram

a Complete this formula for the cost, £ C.

$$C = \boxed{}$$

Let w stand for the weight of the strawberries in kilograms.

b Copy this table.

w	0	1	2	3	4	5	6
C	0				8		

Use the formula to complete it.

c Copy the graph.

Use your table to complete it.

d Join your points with a straight line.

e How much does it cost for 3.5 kg of strawberries?

f John spends £9 on strawberries.

How many kilograms does he buy?

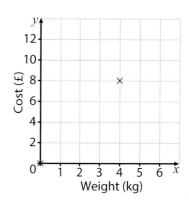

Reasoning

4 Look at the charges for using the Avonford swimming pool and the Fitness Club.

Non-members: Use of pool £2.00

Fitness Club

Membership £20 per year
Use of pool £1 per visit

a Copy and complete this table of values for non-members using the swimming pool.

Number of visits to pool	0	5	10	15	20	25	30
Total cost (£)	0	10					

b Show the information in the table in part **a** as a graph.

c Copy and complete this table of costs for members of the Fitness Club using the swimming pool.

Number of visits to pool	0	5	10	15	20	25	30
Total cost (£)	20	25					

d Show the information in the table in part **c** on the same graph as in part **b**.

e Humza joins the Fitness Club.

He uses the pool twice a week.

After how many weeks does he save money?

5 a Copy and complete these tables.

i

x	0	1	2	3	4
+1	+1	+1	+1	+1	+1
$y = x + 1$	1		3		

ii

x	0	1	2	3	4
+3	+3			+3	
$y = x + 3$	3			6	

iii

x	0	1	2	3	4
+4	+4		+4		
$y = x + 4$	4		6		

iv

x	0	1	2	3	4
+5	+5				+5
$y = x + 5$	5				9

b Draw a pair of axes.

Take x from 0 to 4 and y from 0 to 9.

Draw and label the graphs of **i**, **ii**, **iii** and **iv**.

c What do you notice about your graphs?

d Where would the lines $y = x + 2$ and $y = x + 6$ go?

6 **a** Copy and complete this table.

x	−4	−3	−2	−1	0	1	2	3	4
$y = 5x$	−20			−5					20

b Draw the graph.

c Find the value of y when $x = 1\frac{1}{2}$.

d Find the value of x when $y = 0$.

7 Here is the graph of $y = 2x + 1$.

a What is the value of y when

i $x = 3$

ii $x = 0$

iii $x = 3.5$?

b What is the value of x when

i $y = 11$

ii $y = 6$

iii $y = 9$?

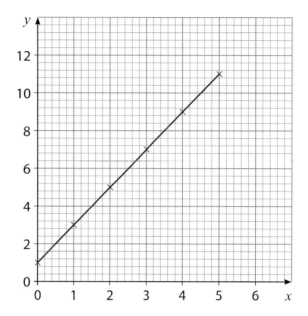

Skills practice B

1 This mapping diagram for $y = 2x$ has been started.

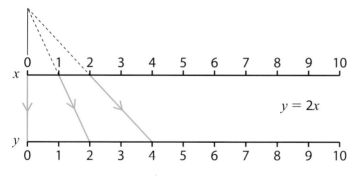

$y = 2x$

a Copy and complete the diagram.

b Two of the arrows have been extended backwards with dotted lines.
Extend all your other arrowed lines in the same way.
What do you notice?

c Draw a mapping diagram for $y = 3x$. Extend the arrowed lines backwards. What do you notice?

2 You are given that $y = 6 - x$.

a Construct a table of values, taking x from 0 to 6.

b Draw a mapping diagram, using the same scale for both x and y.

c When are the values of x and y the same?
How can you see this on your diagram?

d Draw the graph of y against x.

e Describe your graph in words.

Reasoning

3 The time, t minutes, to cook a joint of meat of mass m kilograms is given by this equation.

$t = 20m + 30$

a Copy and complete this table.

m	I	1.5	2	2.5	3	3.5
20m		30				70
+30		30				30
t **= 20m + 30**		60				100

b Draw the graph of t against m.

c Use your graph to find how long to cook a joint of meat with a mass of 0.5 kg.

d A joint of meat takes 85 minute to cook.

Use your graph to find its mass.

4 The height, H, metres of a bookcase depends upon the number of shelves, S, and

$H = 0.3S + 0.1$

a Copy and complete this table.

S	I	2	3	4	5
0.3S		0.6			
+0.1		0.1			
H **= 0.3S + 0.1**		0.7			

b Draw the mapping diagram.

c What is the spacing, in centimetres, between shelves?

d John's bedroom is 2.6 m high.

How many shelves can he have?

5 a Copy and complete this table.

x	−1	0	I	2	3	4	5	6
2x	−2	0						
+5	5	5						
y **= 2x + 5**	3	5						

b Use your table to plot the graph of $y = 2x + 5$.

c Find the value of x when $y = 8$.

6 a Construct a table of values for $y = 5x - 6$ with x from −1 to 3.

b Use your table to plot the graph of $y = 5x - 6$.

c Find the value of y when $x = 2.2$.

7 a Construct a table of values for $y = 5 - x$ with x from −1 to 7.

b Use your table to draw the graph of $y = 5 - x$.

c At which points does the graph cross the x axis and the y axis?

d At which point on the graph are the values of x and y the same?

8 a Draw the graph of $y = 2x$.

b Draw the graph of $y = x + 3$ on the same axes as in part **a**.

c Where do the two lines cross?

9 a Draw axes with values of x from –4 to 4 and values of y from –8 to 8.
Plot the following lines on the same axes.

     i $y = 2x + 8$ **ii** $y = 2x - 8$
     iii $y = 8 - 2x$ **iv** $y = -8 - 2x$

   b What shape have you drawn?

10 Abdul hires a canoe at a boating pond.
Part hours are allowed and you only pay for the time you use!
Maximum hire period is 4 hours

   a Draw a graph of cost against time
      (up to 4 hours) for a canoe.

   b On the same graph add lines for a
      motor boat and a rowing boat.

   c Which is more expensive, a canoe
      or a rowing boat?

Boat hire charges

Type of boat	Fixed charge	Rate per hour
Canoe	£4	£2
Motor boat	£2	£6
Rowing boat	£1	£3

11 a Plot the line $y = 4x$.
Take values of x from –3 to 5.

   b Plot the line $y = -4x$.
Take values of x from –3 to 5.

   c What do you notice?

12 Draw axes with values of x from –2 to 2.
Plot the graphs of $y = 2x + 3$ and $y = -2x + 3$ on your axes.
How are these graphs related?

13 Draw the line $y = 3x - 2$ with values of x from –2 to 3.
Which of these points will not lie on the line?

   a (3, 7)   **b** (10, 28)   **c** (0, 0)   **d** (–5, –13)

Wider skills practice

1 The formula for the perimeter of this rectangle
is Perimeter = 2 × length + 10 m

   a Copy this table.
Use the formula to complete it.

5 m

length

Length (m)	0	1	2	3	4	5	6
Length × 2 (m)	0			6			12
+10	+10	+10	+10	+10	+10	+10	+10
Perimeter (m)	10			16			22

   b Draw axes similar to these ones.
Use them to draw a graph of perimeter against length.

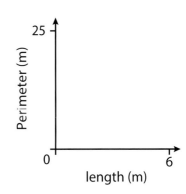

Perimeter (m)

25

0

length (m)

6

2 The thickness, T millimetres, of some children's books is given by

$$T = 4 + \frac{n}{5}$$

where n is the number of pages.

a Copy and complete the table below.

Number of pages, n	10	15	20	25	30	35	40
4	4	4					
$\dfrac{n}{5}$	2	3					
Thickness, T	6	7					

b Draw a mapping diagram to show this relationship.

c What is the thickness of one page?

d The front and back covers of the book are of equal thickness.

How thick is each cover?

3 a Construct a table of values for $y = 5x + 2$ with x from -2 to 6.

b Draw the graph of $y = 5x + 2$.

c A $(0, 2)$ and B $(5, 27)$ are two points on this line.

C is the point $(5, 0)$.

Draw OABC.

What type of quadrilateral is OABC?

4 a Taking x from -2 to 6 and y from -5 to 12, plot the lines $y = 2x - 1$ and $y = 8 - x$ on the same axes.

b Write down the co-ordinates of

i the point A where these lines cross

ii the point B where the line $y = 2x - 1$ crosses the y axis

iii the point C where the line $y = 8 - x$ crosses the y axis

c What is the area of triangle ABC?

5 a Copy and complete this mapping diagram.

The diagrams illustrate the mapping $y = 8 - x$ and $x = 8 - y$.

b What do each of 1, 2, .., 8 map to?

c A mapping like this is called a **self-inverse** mapping. What does this mean?

Chi-Hoo says that any mapping of the form

$$y = c - x$$

where c is a constant, is a self-inverse mapping.

d Make a mapping diagram like the one above for the mapping $y = 5 - x$.

e Do you think Chi-Hoo's statement is true? Explain your answer.

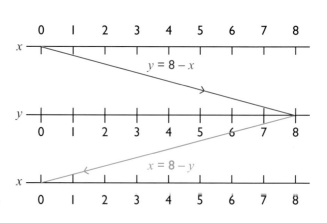

Applying skills

1 The exchange rate for converting Euros into Australian dollars is €1 = A$1.60.

   a Construct a table of values with € from 0 to 60.

   b Draw a conversion graph with 2 cm representing €10 on the x axis and 2 cm representing A$20 on the y axis.

   c Use your graph to convert

     i   €24 to Australian dollars

     ii A$90 to Euros.

Reviewing skills

1 The cost, £y, of x invitation cards to Christina's wedding is given in the table.

Number of invitation cards, x	20	40	60	80	100
Cost in £, y	16	26	36	46	56

   a Plot a graph of this information.

   b Use your graph to estimate

     i   the cost of 55 invitation cards

     ii how many cards can be bought for £42.

2 **a** Draw a mapping diagram for the mapping $y \to 2x - 3$ for values of x from 0 to 7.

   b Now draw the graph of $y = 2x - 3$.

   c Use your graph to find the value of x when $y = 5$.

   d Illustrate your answer to part **c** on the mapping diagram you drew in part **a**.

3 **a** Copy and complete this table of values for $y = 2x - 1$.

x		1	2	3	4	5	6
$2x$		2	4				
-1		-1	-1				
$y = 2x - 1$		1	3				

   b Draw an x axis from 0 to 6 and a y axis from −1 to 12.

     Plot the points from the table of values onto the graph.

     Join them with a straight line.

     Extend the line so that it crosses the y axis.

   c Where does the graph of $y = 2x - 1$ cross the y axis?

   d Will the point (7, 13) be on the graph of $y = 2x - 1$?

     How do you know?

Building skills

Example outside the Maths classroom
Making predictions

Toolbox

Straight-lines have an equation of the form $y = mx + c$.
- The value of m represents the gradient or 'steepness' of the line.
- The value of c tells you where the line crosses the y axis.

Special cases are:
- Horizontal lines which have an equation of the form $y = a$ where a is a number.
- Vertical lines which have an equation of the form $x = b$ where b is a number.

Parallel lines have the same gradient.
The y-intercept is the value where the line cuts the y axis.
To find the gradient of a straight line
1 choose any two points
2 subtract the y co-ordinates
3 subtract the x co-ordinates
4 the gradient is the change in y divided by the change in x.

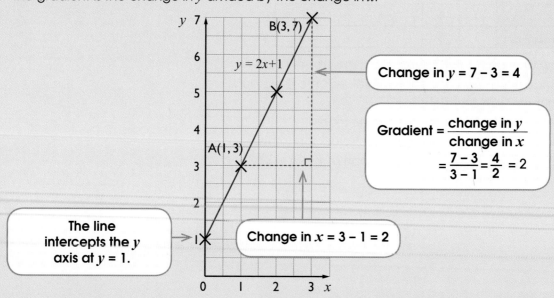

Change in y = 7 − 3 = 4

Gradient = $\dfrac{\text{change in } y}{\text{change in } x}$
$= \dfrac{7-3}{3-1} = \dfrac{4}{2} = 2$

The line intercepts the y axis at $y = 1$.

Change in x = 3 − 1 = 2

If the line slopes down from left to right the gradient is negative.

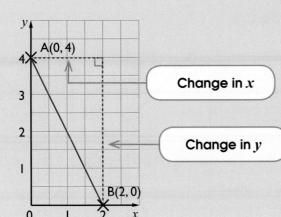

Change in x

Change in y

$$\text{Gradient} = \frac{0 - 4}{2 - 0}$$

$$= \frac{-4}{2} = -2$$

Example – Finding the gradient from the equation of a line

Here are the equations of ten lines.
Write down which ones are parallel.

a $x = 7$

b $y = 3 + 7x$

c $y = 2x + 3$

d $y = -5$

e $y = 2x - 4$

f $x = -2$

g $y = 5 - x$

h $y = -x$

i $y = 7x + 5$

j $y = 4$

Solution

a and **f** ← Vertical lines

b and **i** ← Gradient is 7

c and **e** ← Gradient is 2

d and **j** ← Horizontal lines

g and **h** ← Gradient is −1

Example – Finding an equation from a graph

Match the lines in this diagram with the correct equations.

$x = 3$

$x = -3$

$x = 0$

$y = 3$

$y = -3$

$y = 0$

$y = x + 1$

$y = x - 2$

$y = 2x - 1$

$y = 1 - x$

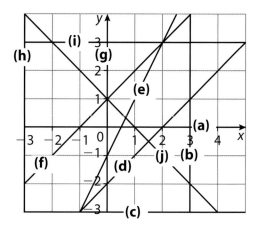

Solution

a is the x axis. Its equation is $y = 0$

b is a vertical line. Every point on the line has an x co-ordinate of 3

c is a horizontal line. Every point on the line has a y co-ordinate of –3. The equation of the line is $y = -3$

d has a gradient of 1 and a y-intercept of -2. The equation of the line is $y = x - 2$

e has a gradient of 2 and a y-intercept of –1. The equation of the line is $y = 2x - 1$

f has a gradient of 1 and a y-intercept of 1. The equation of the line is $y = x + 1$

g is the y axis. Its equation is $x = 0$

h is a vertical line. Every point on the line has an x co-ordinate of –3. The equation of the line is $x = -3$

i is a horizontal line. Every point on the line has a y co-ordinate of 3. The equation of the line is $y = 3$

j has a gradient of –1 and a y-intercept of 1. The equation of the line is $y = -x + 1$ or $y = 1 - x$

Remember:

+ The value of m represents the gradient or 'steepness' of the line.
+ The value of c tells you where the line crosses the y axis.
+ Parallel lines have the same gradient.
+ Lines that slope down have a negative gradient.

Skills practice A

1 P is the point (1, 1) and Q is the point (2, 3).

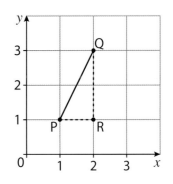

  a Write down the change in y, RQ.

  b Write down the change in x, PR.

  c Use your answers to parts **a** and **b** to work out the gradient of the line PQ.

2 a Write down the co-ordinates of four points marked on each of the lines in these diagrams.

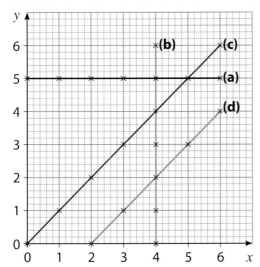

  b Calculate the gradient of each of the lines.

3 a Find the co-ordinates of five points which lie on each of these lines:

    $y = x$ $y = 2x$ $y = 3x$

  b Use your co-ordinates to draw a graph of all the lines on the same axes. Label each line.

  c Calculate the gradient of each line.

  d What do you notice about the gradients of the lines?

  e What is the gradient of the line $y = 20x$?

4 a Copy and complete these tables.

x	−1	0	1	2	3
$3x$		0			9
−2	−2				
$y = 3x - 2$					7

x	−1	0	1	2	3
$2x$	−2		2		
−2	−2	−2		−2	
$y = 2x - 2$	−4				4

  b Draw the graphs of the two lines on the same axes.

  c Write down the y-intercept for each line.

  d Which line is steeper?

5 For each line in this diagram

   a write down the co-ordinates of two points

   b calculate the gradient

   c write down the *y*-intercept

   d match it with one of these equations

      A $y = 3$

      B $x + y = 3$

      C $y = x - 4$

      D $y = x$

      E $x = -4$

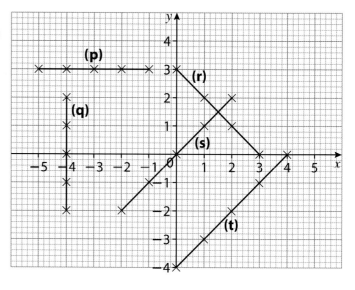

6 a Copy and complete these tables for the lines $y = 2x + 2$ and $y = 2x - 1$.

x	−2	−1	0	1	2	3
2*x*	−4					6
+2	2					2
y = 2*x* + 2	−2					8

x	−2	−1	0	1	2	3
2*x*		−2			4	
−1		−1			−1	
y = 2*x* − 1		−3			3	

   b Draw and label these two lines on the same axes.

   c Write down the co-ordinates of the *y*-intercept for each line.

   d What can you say about the gradients of these two lines?
     How can you tell this from your graph?

   e Draw and complete similar tables for $y = 2x$ and $y = 2x + 4$.

   f What are the co-ordinates of the *y*-intercept of the line $y = 2x + 5$? How can you tell?

7 a Find the missing co-ordinates for these lines.

    i (0, 0), (1, 1), (2, 2), (3, ☐), (☐, 5), (5.5, ☐)

    ii (6, 0), (5, 1), (4, 2), (3, ☐), (☐, 4), (1.5, ☐)

    iii (−1, 1), (0, 2), (1, 3), (2, ☐), (☐, 5), (3.5, ☐)

    iv (−2, 5), (−1, 5), (0, 5), (1, 5), (☐, 5), (3, ☐)

   b Find an equation for each line.

8 For each of the following sets of points,

   a plot them on graph paper and draw a straight line through them

   b find the equation of the line.

    i (−5, −5), (−4, −4), (−3, −3), (−2, −2)

    ii (9, 6), (8, 5), (7, 4), (6, 3)

    iii (4, 3), (3, 4), (2, 5), (1, 6)

Reasoning

Reasoning

9 **a** Draw the graphs of these lines on the same axes.
   Take values of x and y from 0 to 5.
   $x = 4$ $x = 2$ $y = 5$ $y = 3$

  b Which of the lines are parallel to the x axis?
   Which of the lines are parallel to the y axis?

  c What are the equations of the x axis and y axis?

Skills practice B

1 Look at this diagram.
   Shape ABCD is a square.

  a What are the co-ordinates of point D?

  b Which of the points A, B, C and D are on these lines?
   i $x = 2$ **ii** $x = 7$ **iii** $y = 7$
   iv $y = 2$ **v** $y = x$ **vi** $x + y = 9$

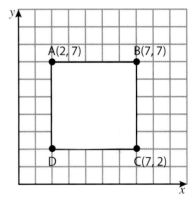

2 **a** Draw x and y axes from 0 to 8.
   On your axes draw the pattern formed by these lines.
   $x = 2$ $x = 5$ $y = 2$
   $y = 5$ $y = x$ $x + y = 7$

  b Draw more lines to divide the diagram into eight triangles of the same size.

  c Write down the equations of the lines you drew in part **b**.

3 Work out the gradient of the line joining each of these pairs of points.

  a (5, 7) and (7, 11)

  b (−4, 2) and (2, 4)

  c (7, 9) and (12, −1)

  d (−8, −2) and (−3, −7)

4 **a** Draw the lines with these equations on the same axes.
   $y = 2x + 2$ $y = x + 4$ $y = 2x − 3$
   $y = 4 + 2x$ $y = x + 2$ $y = x − 3$

  b Which lines have the same gradient?
   What do you notice about their equations?

  c Which pairs of lines have the same y-intercept?
   What do you notice?

  d A line has a gradient of 3 and y-intercept of −5.
   What is its equation?

Reasoning

5 Write down the gradient of each of these lines.

a $y = 4x$ **b** $y = 10x$ **c** $y = 7x$

d $y = \frac{1}{2}x$ **e** $y = -2x$ **f** $y = -x$

g $y = 2x - 1$ **h** $y = 7 + 3x$ **i** $y = 4 + 8x$

j $y = 5 - 3x$

6 Write down the co-ordinates of the y-intercept and the gradient of each of these lines.

a $y = x + 4$ **b** $y = x - 1$ **c** $y = 2x + 3$

d $y = 2x + 5$ **e** $y = 3x + 2$ **f** $y = 5x + 3$

g $y = 3x - 4$ **h** $y = 4x - 5$ **i** $y = 7x + 6$

j $y = 5 - 10x$

7 Find the gradient and y-intercept of each of these lines.
Then write down the equation of the line.

a
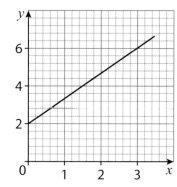

b
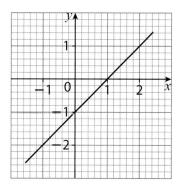

c
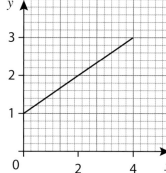

d
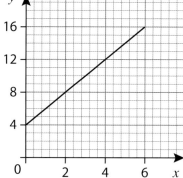

e
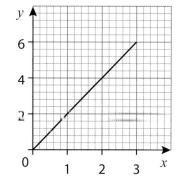

170

8 Here are the equations of eight lines.

$y = 2x + 3$ $y = 3x + 2$ $y = 2x - 3$ $y = 3x - 2$

$y = 4x + 3$ $y = 5x - 4$ $y = 4x$ $y = 3 - 4x$

Choose the equation or equations that produce

a a line that passes through the origin

b a line that has a gradient of 3

c a line that has a gradient of 2

d a line that passes through the point (0, 3)

e the line with the greatest slope

f a line that is parallel to $y = 4x$

g a line with a negative gradient

h a line that passes through the point (0, –4)

i a line that is parallel to $y = 5 - 4x$

j a line that passes through the point (1, 5).

9 a Draw x and y axes with values from –2 to 8 on each axis.

Plot the line with gradient 2 and with an intercept on the y axis of 1.

Write down the equation of this line in the form $y = mx + c$.

b On the same axes, plot the line with gradient 3 and with an intercept on the y axis of –2.

Write down the equation of this line in the form $y = mx + c$.

c Extend your lines so that they cross.

Write down the co-ordinates of the point where the lines cross.

10 Write down the gradient and the co-ordinates of the intercept on the y axis of each of these lines.

a $y = 8 + 3x$ **b** $y = 7 - 2x$ **c** $y = 2(x + 1)$

d $y = \frac{2}{3} + \frac{1}{2}x$ **e** $y = \frac{1}{2}(2x - 5)$ **f** $2y = 6x - 5$

g $x + y = 2$ **h** $2x - y = 7$

Reasoning

Wider skills practice

1 Look at these road signs.

a Which hill is steepest?

b Which hill is least steep?

2 Here are the equations of three lines:

$y = x$ $y = 3 - x$ $y = x + 3$

a Which of these lines are parallel?

b What is the gradient of the two parallel lines?

c Which of the lines have the same y-intercept?

d What are the co-ordinates of the two points where one line crosses the other two?

e Which lines are perpendicular?

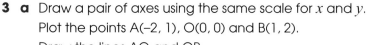
Reasoning

3 **a** Draw a pair of axes using the same scale for x and y.
   Plot the points A(–2, 1), O(0, 0) and B(1, 2).
   Draw the lines AO and OB.

   b Measure angle AOB.

   c Work out the gradients of the lines AO and OB.

   d Repeat parts **a** to **c** for these sets of points.
   i A(–3, 1), O(0, 0), B(1, 3)
   ii A(1, 2), O(0, 0), B(2, –1)
   iii A(1, 3), O(0, 0), B(3, –1)

   e In each case, what do you notice about gradient of AO × gradient of OB?

   f The line AO has a gradient of 4.
   Write down the gradient of the line OB, which is perpendicular to AO.

4 **a** Copy and complete this table for $y = 2x + 2$.

x	–2	–1	0	1
$2x$				
$+2$				
$y = 2x + 2$				

   b Copy and complete this table for $y = -\dfrac{x}{2} + 2$.

x	–2	0	2	4	6
$-\dfrac{x}{2}$					
$+2$					
$y = -\dfrac{x}{2} + 2$					

   c Draw axes with values of x from –3 to 6 and y from –3 to 4.
   Draw the lines $y = 2x + 2$ and $y = -\dfrac{x}{2} + 2$ on your axes.

   d Label the following points and write down their co-ordinates.
   Point A – where the two lines cross.
   Point B – where $y = 2x + 2$ crosses the x axis.
   Point C – where $y = -\dfrac{x}{2} + 2$ crosses the x axis.

   e What is the size of angle BAC in degrees?

   f What is the area of triangle ABC?

Reasoning

5 Helen and David are doing a physics experiment.

They are investigating how forces stretch springs.

David hangs a weight of 1 newton (N) on the end of a spring and measures its length in millimeters.

They then take it in turns to add more weights, each time measuring the length, L mm, of the spring and the force, F N, until there is a total weight of 8 N hanging on it.

Helen and David display their results in a table.

Force, F (N)	0	1	2	3	4	5	6	7	8
Length of spring, L (mm)		36	48	59	71	83	100	106	117

   a Plot the graph of force against length, with force along the horizontal axis.
   Draw a line of best fit.

   b One of the results is wrong.
   Which one do you think it is?
   Suggest the correct value for this result.

   c David forgot to measure the length of the spring before he started hanging weights on it.
   Use your graph to find the length of the spring.

   d Calculate the gradient of the graph.

   e Write the equation of the line in the form $L = \boxed{} F + \boxed{}$

6 Liz and Danny do an experiment with an elastic string.

They measure the extension of the string each time they add a weight to it.

Here are their results.

Force, F (N)	0	2	4	6	8	10	12	14
Extension of string, E (mm)	0	19	39	56	75	95	115	133

   a Plot the graph of force, F N, against extension, E mm, with force along the horizontal axis.

   b Calculate the gradient of the line and use it to write down the equation of the line.

   c What does your graph tell you about the relationship between E and F?

7 Shelley and Rob are doing an electricity experiment in their physics lesson.

They set up a circuit to measure the current, I, flowing through a resistor and the voltage, V, across it.

Their circuit is shown in the diagram.

They set their power pack at 0 volts and record the readings shown on the voltmeter and the ammeter.

Shelley turns the control on the power pack to increase the voltage.

Rob records the new readings on both the voltmeter and the ammeter.

They repeat this several times.

Here are their results.

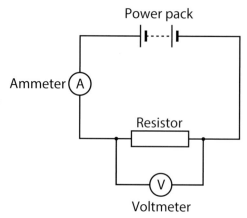

Voltage, V (volts)	Current, I (amps)	$V \div I$
0.0	0.0	–
1.0	0.2	
2.0	0.4	
3.0	0.5	
4.0	0.8	
5.0	1.0	
6.0	1.2	

a Draw a graph of V against I, with I along the horizontal axis.

b Rob wrote an incorrect value for one of the results.

   i Which result is it?

   ii What should you do about it?

c What is the current when the voltage is 4.5 V?

d What is the voltage when the current is 1.1 A?

e The resistance of the resistor is measured in ohms.

The resistance equals the gradient of the line on the graph.

Calculate the resistance.

8 Draw x and y axes.

Use the same scale on each axis and take values from −2 to 6.

a Plot the points A(−2, −2), B(−1, 5), C(3, 6) and D(2, −1).

b Work out the gradient of the lines AB, BC, DC and AD.

c What type of quadrilateral is ABCD?

Applying skills

1   On the graph below a point has been plotted and five lines drawn through it.
    Draw a graph and plot a point of your choice.
    Investigate the equations of lines which pass through your point.

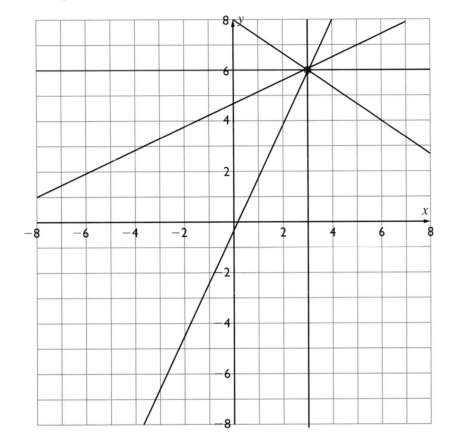

2   Avonford Autos are a car-hire company.
    The basic charge is £20 plus a further 30p per mile.
    a   Show that $C = 0.3x + 20$, where C is the cost of driving x miles.
    b   Plot a graph of this equation for values of x from 0 to 200.
    c   Use your graph to find the cost of hiring a car and driving 80 miles.
    d   Use your graph to find how many miles are driven when the hire cost is £56.

3   Gas bills have a standing charge of £15 plus 10p per gas unit used.
    The bill is £B.
    a   Show this is related to x, the number of gas units used, by the equation $B = 15 + 0.1x$.
    b   Plot a graph of this equation taking x values from 0 to 800.
    c   Use your graph to find Mr Smith's bill when he uses 275 units of gas.
    d   The Butterworths' bill is £89.
        Use your graph to find how many units of gas they used.

4 Work out the gradient of the line *PQ* shown in each of these diagrams.

a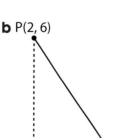

b P(2, 6)

c

P(2, 2) ———————— Q(5, 2)

Reviewing skills

1 Match the lines in this diagram with the correct equations.

i $x = 2$

ii $y = 3$

iii $y = -x$

iv $y = x + 1$

v $y = 5$

vi $x = -2$

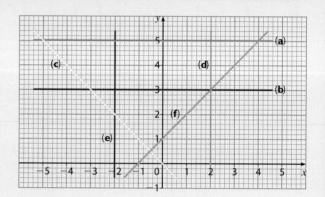

2 Here are the graphs of the lines $y = x - 2$ and $y = 2x$.

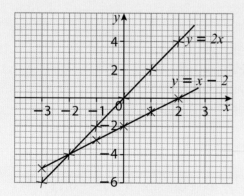

a Find the gradient of each line.

b Which is the steeper line?

c Find the y-intercept of each line.

d Write down the co-ordinates of the point where the two lines cross.

3 Here are the equations of eight lines.

$y = 2x - 3$ $x + y = 5$ $3y = 6x + 10$

$y + 3x = 0$ $y = -3$ $y = 3 - x$

$y = 3x + 5$ $y = 4x - 7$

Choose the equations of the lines which have

a a y-intercept at $(0, 0)$

b a gradient of 0

c a negative gradient

d a gradient of 3

e a gradient of 2

f a gradient of -3

g the steepest slope

h a y-intercept at $(0, 5)$

4 a Draw x and y axes.

Take values from -2 to 8 on each axis.

b Plot the line whose gradient is 1 and whose intercept on the y axis is 2.

c Plot the line whose gradient is 2 and whose intercept on the y axis is -2.

d Write down the co-ordinates of the point where these two lines meet.

e Plot the line whose gradient is $\frac{1}{2}$ and whose intercept on the y axis is 4.

What do you notice about this line?

Building skills

Toolbox

Equations which contain powers of x greater than 1 (e.g. x^2, x^3) are not linear functions; instead they produce curved lines.

Equations with x^2 terms but no x^3 terms produce **quadratic** curves.

x	−3	−2	−1	0	1	2	3
$y = x^2$	9	4	1	0	1	4	9

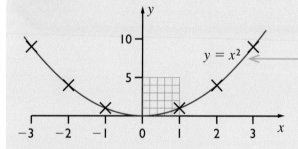

The points are joined by a smooth curve.

Equations with x^3 terms produce **cubic** curves.

x	−3	−2	−1	0	1	2	3
$y = x^3$	−27	−8	−1	0	1	8	27

The points are joined by a smooth curve.

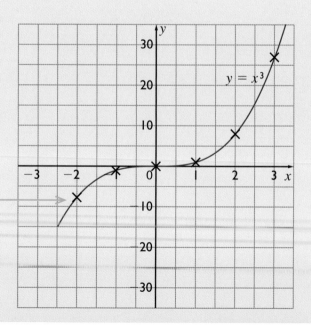

Example – Drawing and using quadratic curves

a Make a table of values for $y = x^2 - 4x + 1$, taking values of x from -1 to 5.

b Draw the graph of $y = x^2 - 4x + 1$.

c Use your graph to solve the equation $x^2 - 4x + 1 = 0$.

Solution

a

x	-1	0	1	2	3	4	5
x^2	1	0	1	4	9	16	25
$-4x$	4	0	-4	-8	-12	-16	-20
$+1$	1	1	1	1	1	1	1
$y = x^2 - 4x + 1$	6	1	-2	-3	-2	1	6

b

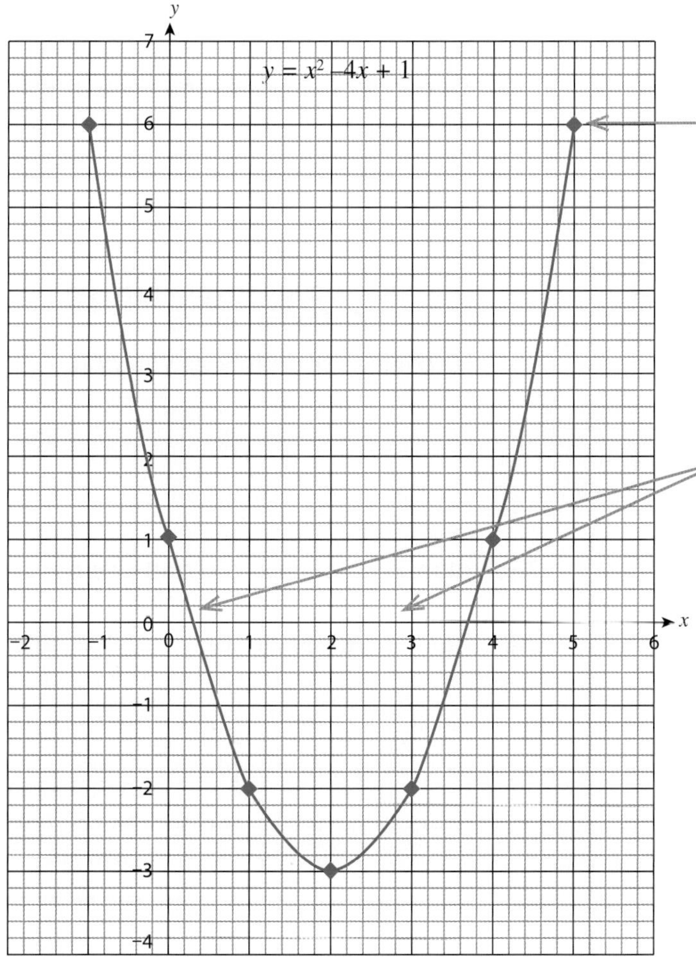

$y = x^2 - 4x + 1$

> All quadratic equations produce a curve in the shape of a parabola.
>
> Draw it as smoothly as you can.

> The curve crosses the line $y = 0$ at approximately $x = 0.3$ and $x = 3.7$.

> The solution to the equation $x^2 - 4x + 1 = 0$ is given by the x values at the points where the curve crosses the x axis (the line $y = 0$).
>
> Values taken from a graph are only approximate.

c $x = 0.3$ or $x = 3.7$

Example – Drawing and using cubic curves

a Make a table of values for $y = x^3 - 5x$, taking values of x from -3 to 3.

b Draw the graph of $y = x^3 - 5x$.

c Find the values of x where this curve crosses the x axis.

d Write down the solution of the equation $x^3 - 5x = 0$.

Solution

a

x	-3	-2	-1	0	1	2	3
x^3	-27	-8	-1	0	1	8	27
$-5x$	15	10	5	0	-5	-10	-15
$y = x^3 - 5x$	-12	2	4	0	-4	-2	12

b

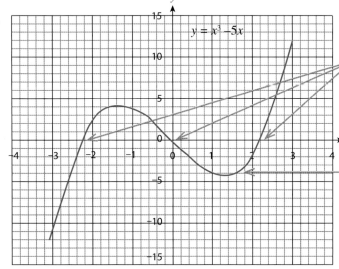

The curve crosses the line $y = 0$ at $x = 0$ and approximately $x = -2.2$ and $x = 2.2$.

All cubic equations produce an S-shaped curve.

Draw it as smoothly as you can.

c $x = 0$, $x = -2.2$ or $x = 2.2$

The value $x = 0$ is accurate and you could have found it from your table.

The other two values are only approximate.

Remember:

✦ Quadratic and cubic graphs should be drawn using smooth curves.

Skills practice A

1 a Copy and complete this table for $y = x^2 - 2$.

x	−3	−2	−1	0	1	2	3
x^2	9	4					9
−2	−2	−2					−2
$y = x^2 - 2$	7	2					7

b What is the name of this type of equation?

c Draw axes with values of x from −3 to 3 and y from −3 to 8.
   Plot the points from your table and join them with a smooth curve.

2 a Copy and complete this table for $y = 10 - x^2$.

x	−4	−3	−2	−1	0	1	2	3	4
10	10	10	10						
$-x^2$	−16	−9	−4						
$y = 10 - x^2$	−6	1	6						

> Work out x^2 first and then make it negative.

b Plot the points and join them with a smooth curve.

3 a Copy and complete this table for $y = 3x^2 + 7$.

x		−1	0	1	2	3
$3x^2$		3	0			
+7		7	7			
$y = 3x^2 + 7$		10	7			

> Work out x^2 first and then multiply by 3.

b Draw the graph of $y = 3x^2 + 7$.

c Use your graph to estimate the value of x when $y = 15$.

4 a Copy and complete this table for $y = (x - 3)^2$.

x	−1	0	1	2	3	4	5	6	7
$x - 3$	−4	−3	−2						
$y = (x - 3)^2$	16	9	4						

b Draw the graph of $y = (x - 3)^2$.

c What is the equation of the line of symmetry of the curve?

Skills practice B

1 a Copy and complete this table of values.

x		−3	−2	−1	0	1	2	3
$4x^2$		36	16					
$+9$		9	9					
$y = 4x^2 + 9$		45	25					

b Draw axes, taking x from −3 to 3 and y from 0 to 50.
Plot the graph of $y = 4x^2 + 9$.

c What is the minimum value that y takes?

2 a Copy and complete this table of values.

x		−4	−3	−2	−1	0	1	2	3	4
$3x^2$		48	27							
$+2$		2	2							
$y = 3x^2 + 2$		50	29							

b Draw the graph of $y = 3x^2 + 2$.

c Use your graph to estimate the value of y when $x = 2.5$.

3 a Copy and complete this table of values.

x	−3	−2	−1	0	1	2	3
x^3	−27	−8					
$+4$	4	4					
$y = x^3 + 4$	−23	−4					

b Draw the graph of $y = x^3 + 4$.

4 a Copy and complete this table of values for $y = 6x - x^2$.

x		−1	0	1	2	3	4	5	6	7
$6x$		−6	0							
$-x^2$		−1	0							
$y = 6x - x^2$		−7	0							

b Draw the points and join them with a smooth curve.

c Use your graph to solve the equation $6x - x^2 + 3 = 0$.

5 a Copy and complete this table of values.

x	−1	0	1	2	3	4	5	6	7	8
$7x$	−7	0								
$-x^2$	−1	0								
$y = 7x - x^2$	−8	0								

b Decide on suitable scales and draw x and y axes.
Plot the graph of $y = 7x - x^2$.

c What is the equation of the line of symmetry of this graph?

d What is the greatest value of y?

Wider skills practice

1 a Copy and complete this table.

x	−4	−3	−2	−1	0	1	2	3	4
20	20	20	20						
$-x^2$	−16	−9	−4						
$y = 20 - x^2$	4	11	16						

b Draw the graph of $y = 20 - x^2$.

c This graph has a line of symmetry.
What is the equation of this line?

d When would you expect to see a curve with this shape in real life?

2 a Construct a table of values for $y = x^3$ with x from −3 to 3.

b Plot the graph of $y = x^3$.

c Describe the symmetry of this graph.

d Now draw the graph of $y = x^3 + 2$ on the same axes.

e Describe the transformation that maps $y = x^3$ on to $y = x^3 + 2$.

3 a Copy and complete this table.

x		0	1	2	3	4
x^2				4		
$-4x$				−8		
$+4$				4		
$y = x^2 - 4x + 4$				0		

b Draw a set of axes with values of x from 0 to 4 and values of y from −4 to 4.
Draw the graph of $y = x^2 - 4x + 4$.

c Use your graph to solve the equation $x^2 - 4x + 4 = 0$.

d Draw the reflection of the curve in the x axis.

e What are the co-ordinates of the image of the points (0, 4), (2, 0) and (4, 4)?

f Do any of the points on the curve stay the same under the reflection?

Reasoning

4 Marion lies on top of a cliff and throws a stone into the air.
The stone moves so that its height, y metres, above Marion after a time of x seconds is given by $y = 20x - 5x^2$.

a Copy and complete this table of values.

x	0	1	2	3	4	5	6
$20x$			40				
$-5x^2$	0	-5	-20				-180
$y = 20x - 5x^2$			20				

Work out x^2 first, then multiply by –5.

b Plot the points and join them with a smooth curve.
c What is the greatest height the stone reaches?
d When does this happen?
e For how long is the stone above Marion?
f What happens after that?
g The stone hits the beach after six seconds.
How high is the cliff?
h When is the stone 4m above Marion?
i When is the stone 16m above Marion?
j For how long is the stone more than 16m above Marion?

5 A company makes rectangular mats.
The lengths of the mats are 60 centimetres greater than their widths.

a Show that the area A cm², of a mat is $A = x^2 + 60x$.
b Copy and complete this table:

x	0	20	40	60	80	100
x^2		400				
$60x$		1200				
$A = x^2 + 60x$		1600				

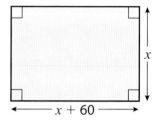

$x + 60$

c Plot a graph of A against x.
d Estimate the dimensions of a mat which has an area of 14000 cm².

6 a Copy and complete this table for $y = (x - 2)(x - 4)$.
b Draw the graph of $y = (x - 2)(x - 4)$.

x	0	1	2	3	4	5	6
$x - 2$	-2	-1					
$x - 4$	-4	-3					
$y = (x - 2)(x - 4)$	8	3					

c What is the equation of the line of symmetry of this graph?
d Label the points A(0, 8), B(2, 0) and C(4, 0) on the curve.
Draw triangle ABC and find its area.

Applying skills

1 The flight of a football during a free kick is given by the equation $h = 4t - t^2$, where h is the height of the ball, in metres, after t seconds.

   a Plot a graph of this information for values of t from 0 to 4 seconds.

   b What is the greatest height of the ball?

   c The ball reaches the goal-line at time $t = 3.8$ seconds.
   The goals are 2 metres high.
   Could this free kick result in a goal?

2 The formula for the volume, V cm^3, of a square-based pyramid

   is $V = \frac{1}{3}b^2h$

   where b cm is the base length and h cm is the perpendicular height.

   a A toy company produces wooden square-based pyramids with a perpendicular height of 6 cm.
   Find a formula for V in terms of b.

   b Plot the graph of V against b for values of b from 0 to 4 cm.

   c Use your graph to estimate the value of b when $V = 20$.

   d How could you have found the answer to part c without drawing a graph?

3 A cargo ship transports an oil consignment at a speed of v kilometres per hour.

   At this speed the cost, £C, of a 300-kilometre trip is $C = 25v + \dfrac{8000}{v}$.

   a Copy and complete this table.

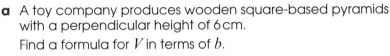
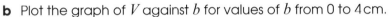

v	10	15	20	25	30	35	40
$25v$	250		500				1000
$\dfrac{8000}{v}$	800		400				200
$C = 25v + \dfrac{8000}{v}$	1050		900				1200

   b Draw a graph of C against v.

   c Use your graph to estimate:

   i the cost of a journey at 27.5 km/hr

   ii the speed at which the cost is least.

4 a i Draw the graphs of $y = x^2 + 2$ and $y = x^2 + 5$ for values of x from −3 to 3.

   ii Use your graphs to explain the effect of c in the equation $y = x^2 + c$.

   b i Draw the graphs of $y = 2x^2$ and $y = 3x^2$ for values of x from −3 to 3.

   ii Use your graphs to explain the effect of a in the equation $y = ax^2$.

Reviewing skills

1 **a** Copy and complete this table of values.

x	–3	–2	–1	0	1	2	3
x^2	9	4					
$-2x$	6	4					
-3	–3	–3					
$y = x^2 - 2x - 3$	12	5					

   b Plot the points and join them with a smooth curve.

   c What is the minimum value that y takes?

2 **a** Draw the graph of $y = x^2 - 4x + 3$.
   Take values of x from –1 to 5.

   b What is the equation of the line of symmetry of the curve?

   c What is the least possible value for $x^2 - 4x + 3$?

   d Use your graph to solve the equation $x^2 - 4x + 3 = 0$.

Strand 4 • Algebraic methods

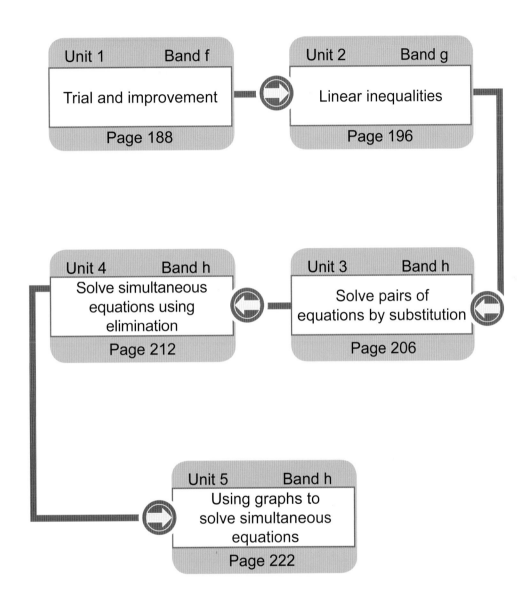

Unit 1   Band f

Trial and improvement

Page 188

Unit 2   Band g

Linear inequalities

Page 196

Unit 4   Band h

Solve simultaneous equations using elimination

Page 212

Unit 3   Band h

Solve pairs of equations by substitution

Page 206

Unit 5   Band h

Using graphs to solve simultaneous equations

Page 222

Building skills

Example outside the Maths classroom

Solving complex problems

Toolbox

When an equation cannot be solved algebraically you can use trial and improvement to solve it. Trial and improvement means you make a sensible first guess (trial) and then you improve upon it.

Once you have found that the solution lies between two consecutive values, you should check the value halfway between them.

$x = 8$ too small

$x = 9$ too big

Try $x = 8.5$ next.

Keep repeating the process until you have the degree of accuracy you need.

$x = 8.2$ too small

$x = 8.3$ too big

$x = 8.25$ too small

x is between 8.25 and 8.3, so $x = 8.3$ to 1 d.p.

Example – Solving a problem

Zac is designing a tray to hold 75 cm³ of sugar.

The width is 3 times the height.

The length is 4 times the height.

Zac makes a table to find x.

Find x correct to 1 decimal place.

x	$3x$	$4x$	Volume	Too big or too small?
1	3	4	12 cm³	small
2	6	8	96 cm³	
1.5				

Solution

When $x = 1.5$, volume = 40.5 cm³ ← **too small**

$x = 1.8$, volume = 69.9... cm³ ← **too small**

$x = 1.9$, volume = 82.3... cm³ ← **too big**

$x = 1.85$, volume = 75.9... cm³ ← **too big**

So $x = 1.8$ to 1 d.p. In the end Zac decides to use 1.9 to be on the safe side.

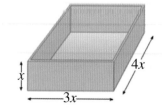

Example – Solving an equation

Zac wants to solve

$$x^2 + \frac{1}{x} = 11$$

correct to 2 d.p.

Here is part of Zac's table of results.

Find the value of x correct to 2 d.p.

x	3.27	3.28	3.275
$x^2+\frac{1}{x}=11$	10.99...	11.06...	11.03...

Solution

The table shows that x is greater than 3.27 but less than 3.275.

Any number in this range rounds to 3.27 to 2 d.p.

So $x = 3.27$ to 2 d.p.

 Remember:

+ First make a sensible guess (trial) and test it.
+ If you know the solution lies between two numbers, then your next trial is to test the mid-point of these numbers.
+ Keep running trials until you have the required level of accuracy.

Skills practice A

1 Karl and Harry are playing a game of *Guess my number*.
 a What should Karl's first guess be?

 Harry says it is too small.
 b What should Karl guess next?

My number is between 1 and 9.

Harry

2 Megan is estimating square roots.

Megan

The square root of 13 is between 3 and 4. I know, because $3^2 = 9$ and $4^2 = 16$.

$3^2 = 3 \times 3 = 9$
So the square root of 9 is 3.

Which whole numbers does the square root of each of these numbers lie between?
 a 19 **b** 55 **c** 90 **d** 130

3 John and Michelle are working out the length of this square.

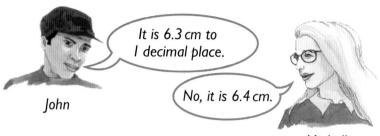

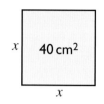

John

Michelle

   a Calculate these.

     i 6.3×6.3 **ii** 6.4×6.4

   b What is the difference between your answer to part **a i** and 40?
     What about your answer to part **a ii** and 40?

   c Who is right? Why?

4 Karl and Sophie are working out the length of this cube.

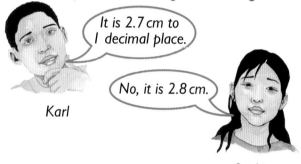

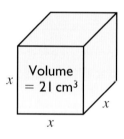

Karl

Sophie

   a Calculate these.

     i $2.7 \times 2.7 \times 2.7$ **ii** $2.8 \times 2.8 \times 2.8$

   b What is the difference between your answer to part **a i** and 21?
     What about between your answer to part **a ii** and 21?

   c Who is right? Why?

5 Work out the length of this cube.
   Give your answer to 1 decimal place.
   Use a copy of this table for your calculations.

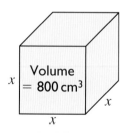

x^3	Calculation	Small / Large
7	$7 \times 7 \times 7 = 343$	Too small
10		

Skills practice B

1 Work out the lengths of these squares.
Give your answers to 1 decimal place.

a

x | 20 cm²

x

b

x | 60 cm²

x

c

x | 120 cm²

x

2 Copy and complete the table to solve the equation $x^2 + x = 25$.
Give your answer to 1 decimal place.

x	x^2	$x^2 + x$	Small / Large
4	4 × 4 = 16	16 + 4 = 20	too small
5	5 × 5 = 25	25 + 5 = 30	too large
4.5			

3 Copy and complete the table to solve the equation $x^2 - x = 50$.
Give your answer to 1 decimal place.

x	x^2	$x^2 - x$	Small / Large
7	7 × 7 = 49	49 − 7 = 42	too small
8	8 × 8 = 64	64 − 8 = 56	too large
7.5			

4 Copy and complete the table to solve the equation $x^2 + 2x = 110$.
Give your answer to 1 decimal place.

x	x^2	$2x$	$x^2 + 2x$	Small / Large
9	9 × 9 = 81	18	81 + 18 = 99	too small
10	10 × 10 = 100	20	100 + 20 = 120	too large
9.5				

5 Make tables to solve these equations.
Give your answers to 2 decimal places.

a $x + x^2 = 150$

b $2x^2 + x = 75$

c $x(1 + x) = 150$

d Explain your answers to parts **a** and **c**.

6 Follow the flowchart to find a pair of numbers with a sum of 10 and a product of 20.

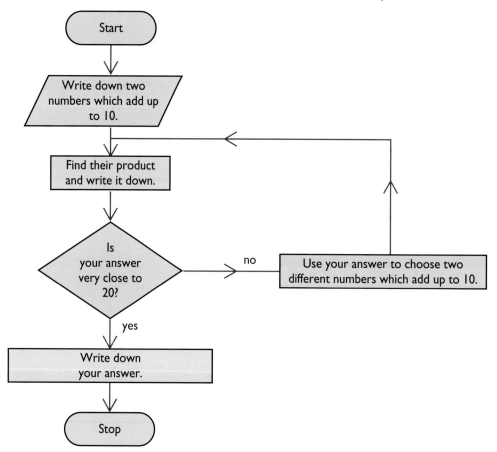

7 The product of three consecutive numbers is 4896.
Find the three numbers.

Wider skills practice

1 This sheet of cardboard has an area of 20 cm².

a Show that $x^2 - 2x = 20$.

b Show that $x = 5$ is too small.

c Show that $x = 6$ is too large.

d Copy and complete this table to find x correct to 2 decimal places.

x	x^2	$-2x$	Area	Small / Large
5				
6				
5.1				

2 This triangle has an area of 23 cm².

    a Show that $h^2 + 4h = 46$.

    b Show that $h = 5$ is too small.

    c Show that $h = 6$ is too large.

    d Copy and complete this table to find h correct to 2 decimal places.

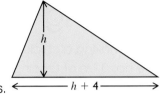

h	h^2	$4h$	Area	Small / Large
5				
6				

3 This trapezium has an area of 59 cm².

    a Show that $h^2 + 3h = 59$.

    b Show that $h = 6$ is too small.

    c Show that $h = 7$ is too large.

    d Find h correct to 2 decimal places.
       You can use a spreadsheet to help you.

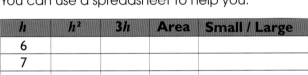

h	h^2	$3h$	Area	Small / Large
6				
7				

4 Alan is making a rectangular flower bed.
The length is 4 m more than the width.
The width is x metres.

    a Write down an expression for the length in terms of x.

    b Write down an expression in x for the area of the rectangle.

The area of the flower bed is 36 m².

    c Write down an equation in x for the area of the flower bed.

    d Use trial and improvement to solve this equation correct to 1 decimal place.

    e What length and width does Alan make his flower bed?

5 Avonford Council have approved the building of an aviary
in the local park.
It will have a square floor and a volume of 500 m³.
It will have four sides and a roof of netting.

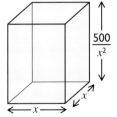

    a The length of one edge of the floor is x metres.
       Explain why the height of the aviary will be $\dfrac{500}{x^2}$ metres.

    b The park manager states that the area of netting in square metres

       will be $x^2 + \dfrac{2000}{x}$

       Explain his working.

    c Find the value of x, to the nearest 0.01, for the least area of netting.

Reasoning

Applying skills

1 Kim is making a chicken run against a long wall.
She has 32 m of fencing.
Kim wants to make the largest possible area.
She writes this equation

$l + 2w = 32$

a What do l and w stand for?

Kim tries different lengths for her chicken run.

When $l = 2$

$2 + 2w = 32$

b When the length is 2 m, what is the width?
What is the area of the chicken run?

c Copy and complete Kim's table.

Length, l	Equation	Width, w	Area = $l \times w$
2	$2 + 2w = 32$		
4	$4 + 2w = 32$	14	56
6			
8			

d What is the largest possible area for the chickens?

2 Sunita is making a tray. She uses a 20 cm square piece of card.
She cuts a square out of each corner and folds the card into a tray.

I want the tray to hold as much as possible.

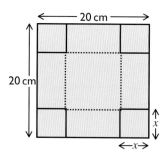

a Copy and complete Sunita's table of values.
Find the value of x that gives the largest volume.
Give your answer to 2 decimal places.

x cm	Volume (cm³)
2	$16 \times 16 \times 2 = 512$
3	$14 \times 14 \times 3 = 588$

b Why must the value of x always be less than 10 cm?

Reviewing skills

1   Copy the table and continue it to solve the equation $x^3 + 2x = 100$.

Find the value of x to 2 decimal places.

x	x^3	$2x$	$x^3 + 2x$	Small / Large
4	64	8	64 + 8 = 72	too small
5	125	10	125 + 10 = 135	too large
4.5				

2   Solve these equations.

Give your answers to 1 decimal place.

a $x^3 - x^2 = 100$

b $x^3 + x = 50$

3   William is designing a new milk carton in the shape of a cube.

It must hold $440\,cm^3$.

The length of the cube is $x\,cm$.

a   Write an equation in terms of x for the volume of the cube.

b   Solve your equation to find the length of the cube to 1 decimal place.

Building skills

Example outside the Maths classroom

Manufacturing constraints

Toolbox

You can use a **number line** to show an **inequality**.
This number line represents $-2 \leqslant x < 3$.

$$-4 \quad -3 \quad -2 \quad -1 \quad 0 \quad 1 \quad 2 \quad 3 \quad 4$$

The integer (whole number) values of x are $-2, -1, 0, 1$ and 2.
These numbers are said to 'satisfy' the inequality.
You solve linear inequalities in the same way that you solve equations, but remember.

* keep the inequality sign pointing the same way

$x + 6 < 7$	$x + 6 < 7$	$x + 6 < 7$
$x < 1$ ✓	$x = 1$ ✗	$x > 1$ ✓

* when you multiply or divide by a negative number, turn the inequality sign round.

$-3x > 12$	$-4x > 12$	$-\frac{1}{2}x \leqslant 2$
$x < -4$ ✓	$x > -3$ ✗	$x > -4$ ✓

Example – Solving a word problem with an inequality

An animal shelter has enough kennels to keep 20 dogs.

They never have fewer than eight dogs.

a Write an inequality for the number of dogs, d, at the shelter.

b Show the inequality on a number line.

Solution

a $8 \leqslant d \leqslant 20$ **Use 'less than or equal to' signs to include 8 and 20.**

b On the number line, draw circles at 8 and 20 and join them with a straight line.
d can equal 8 and 20, so fill in both of the circles.

| 0 | 2 | 4 | 6 | 8 | 10 | 12 | 14 | 16 | 18 | 20 |

Example – Using a number line

a Show the inequality $-1 \leqslant x < 4$ on a number line.
b Write down the possible integer (whole number) values of x.

Solution

a

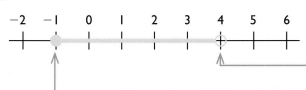

       x must be less than 4 so leave this circle open.

       x can equal –1, so fill in this circle.

b Include –1, but not 4.
The integer values of x are –1, 0, 1, 2 and 3.   **Remember that 0 is a whole number.**

Example – Solving inequalities

Solve these inequalities.

a $5(2x + 3) \geqslant 20$

b $8(x + 1) \leqslant 3x + 18$

c $6 - 3x < 9$

Solution

a $5(2x + 3) \geqslant 20$

$10x + 15 \geqslant 20$ ← Expand the bracket.

$10x \geqslant 5$ ← Subtract 15 from both sides.

$x \geqslant \dfrac{5}{10}$ ← Divide both sides by 10.

$x \geqslant \dfrac{1}{2}$

Check: Let $x = 1$. ← Choose any number greater than or equal to $\dfrac{1}{2}$.

$5(2 \times 1 + 3) \geqslant 20$

$5(2 + 3) \geqslant 20$ ← Calculate the brackets first.

$5 \times 5 \geqslant 20$

$25 > 20$ ✓

b $8(x + 1) \leqslant 3x + 18$

$8x + 8 \leqslant 3x + 18$ ← Expand the brackets.

$5x + 8 \leqslant 18$ ← Subtract $3x$ from both sides.

$5x \leqslant 10$ ← Subtract 8 from both sides.

$x \leqslant 2$ ← Divide both sides by 5.

Check: Let $x = 2$. ← Choose any number less than or equal to 2.

$8(2 + 1) \leqslant 3 \times 2 + 18$

$8 \times 3 \leqslant 6 + 18$ ← Notice that $\leqslant$ means less than or equal to so it is true that $24 \leqslant 24$.

$24 \leqslant 24$ ✓

Let $x = 1$. ← Choose another number less then or equal to 2.

$8(1 + 1) \leqslant 3 \times 1 + 18$

$8 \times 2 \leqslant 3 + 18$

$16 \leqslant 21$ ✓

c In this inequality there is a negative x term.

There are two methods you can use to deal with this.

Method 1

$6 - 3x < 9$

$-3x < 3$ ← Subtract 6 from both sides.

$x > \dfrac{3}{-3}$ ← Divide both sides by −3 and change the direction of the inequality sign.

$x > -1$

Method 2

$6 - 3x < 9$

$\quad 6 < 9 + 3x$ ⟵ **Add 3x to both sides so the x term becomes positive.**

$\quad -3 < 3x$ ⟵ **Subtract 9 from both sides.**

$\quad \dfrac{3}{3} > x$ ⟵ **Divide both sides by 3.**

$\quad -1 < x$

$\quad x > -1$ ⟵ **Turn the inequality around.**

Check: Let $x = 1$. ⟵ **Choose a value of x that is greater than −1.**

$\quad\quad 6 - 3 \times 1 < 9$

$\quad\quad\quad 6 - 3 < 9$

$\quad\quad\quad\quad 3 < 9$ ✓

Remember:

✦ The inequality sign looks a bit like an open mouth.

The small end of the inequality sign points to the smaller value. > $<$ < **The 'mouth' opens towards the greater value.**

✦ When you show an inequality on a number line, a filled-in circle means that number is included.

✦ You solve an inequality like a normal equation, just keep the inequality sign pointing the same way ...

✦ ... but take care when you multiply or divide by a negative number – you need to turn the inequality sign round.

Skills practice A

1 Copy the following pairs of numbers.
Put the correct inequality sign, < or >, between them.

a 7 ☐ 12   **b** 3 ☐ 2   **c** 5.6 ☐ 7.2   **d** 0.3 ☐ 0.2

e −2 ☐ 5   **f** 3 ☐ −7   **g** −6 ☐ −8   **h** −2 ☐ 2

2 Are these statements true or false?

a $5 > 3$ **b** $7 \leqslant 10 - 3$ **c** $6 > 3 \times 2$

d $3.5 \geqslant 7 \div 2$ **e** $5 + 7 < 6 \times 3$ **f** $9 \times 2 \geqslant 10 + 9$

Reasoning

3 Copy the table below. Write these words under the correct inequality sign.

more than	less than or equal to
at least	no less than
no more than	less than
more than or equal to	at most
equal to or under	over
equal to or over	under
lower than	higher than

<	≤	≥	>

4 Match the statements below with the correct inequality.

$x < 3$ $x \geqslant 3$ $x > 3$ $x \leqslant 3$

a x is less than or oqual to 3.

b x has a minimum value of 3.

c x is greater than 3.

d x is less than 3.

e x is at most 3.

f x has a maximum value of 3.

g x is at least 3.

h x is greater than or equal to 3.

i x is no more than 3

5 Write down the inequalities shown on these number lines.

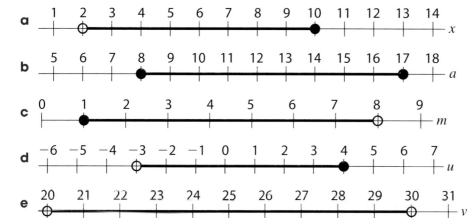

6 Do these actions to both sides of the inequality $-4 < 8$.
Each time, check whether the new inequality is also true.

   a Add 1.

   b Subtract 4.

   c Add 3.

   d Multiply by 2.

   e Subtract 8.

   f Divide by 2.

   g Multiply by 9.

   h Divide by 4.

7 Show each of these inequalities on a number line from 0 to 10.

   a $3 \leqslant x < 7$ **b** $0 < x \leqslant 6$ **c** $7 \leqslant x \leqslant 10$

   d $1 < x \leqslant 5$ **e** $4 < x < 9$ **f** $2 \leqslant x < 8$

8 Solve these inequalities.

   a $3x \leqslant 15$ **b** $2x > 8$ **c** $x + 4 < 10$

   d $x - 6 > 12$ **e** $2x + 4 > 14$ **f** $3x - 3 < 3$

   g $\frac{1}{2}x - 4 < 2$ **h** $8 > x + 3$

Skills practice B

1 The letters A, C, G, I and M all represent numbers where

   G < I   C > A   C > I   M < A   G > A

   Put them in order, starting with the smallest.

2 For each of these inequalities, list all the possible whole number values of x.

   a $3 \leqslant x < 8$

   b $2 < x < 10$

   c $10 \leqslant x \leqslant 15$

   d $0 < x < 8$

   e $0 \leqslant x \leqslant 8$

   f $6.5 < x < 10$

   g $3 \leqslant x < 8.5$

   h $3 \leqslant x < 6.5$

3 Write the information in these situations using inequality symbols.

   a The number of people, p, who went to Pat's party was less than 22.

   b Bob buys l litres of petrol for his car.
      The minimum amount that he can buy is 5 litres and his car has a 45-litre tank.

   c Each house on an estate has either 2, 3, 4 or 5 bedrooms.
      Mr and Mrs Hajba buy a house with b bedrooms.

   d An animal shelter has enough space to keep 25 stray pets.
      One day they have x stray dogs and y stray cats.

Reasoning

4 Write each of these statements as an inequality.

a

Avonford Youth Club

Hockey Team Rules

All players must be at least 12 but less than 16 years old.

All teams in the quiz must have at least three members but no more than eight.

5 Write each of these statements as an inequality.

a

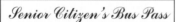

Important Notice

This lift carries a maximum of 12 people.

b

Youth Club Leader needed

Pay from £4 to £9 per hour depending on experience.

c

Senior Citizen's Bus Pass

Anyone 65 years old or over can apply for a senior citizen's bus pass.

d

SHOP MANAGER

Required

All applicants must be over 18 and up to 30 years old.

e

Avonford Music Festival

All choirs must have at least 20 members but no more than 30.

6 Solve these inequalities.

a $2x + 6 < 15$

b $3x + 12 \leqslant 30$

c $4x + 1 \geqslant x + 8$

d $9x + 4 < 5x - 8$

e $9 - 2x > 3$

f $2(x - 5) \leqslant 0$

g $13 - 4x < 5$

h $5(x - 2) < 6x$

i $1 - \frac{1}{2}x \leqslant 3$

7 Solve these inequalities.

a $2x + 5 \geqslant 17$

b $4x - 6 \leqslant 38$

c $4x - 3 > 29$

d $8x + 6 \geqslant 38$

e $3(2x - 3) > 6$

f $4(3x + 2) < 44$

g $3x + 4 \geqslant 16$

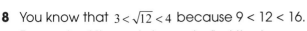
Reasoning

8 You know that $3 < \sqrt{12} < 4$ because $9 < 12 < 16$.

For each of these statements, find the two consecutive whole numbers that make the statement true.

a $\square < \sqrt{27} < \square$

b $\square < \sqrt{86} < \square$

c $\square < \sqrt{150} < \square$

9 Do these actions to both sides of the inequality $-4 < 8$.
Each time, check whether it is necessary to reverse the inequality sign to make the new inequality true.

  a Multiply by -2.   **b** Divide by -2.

  c Add -3.   **d** Subtract -4.

  e Divide by -1.   **f** Multiply by -4.

  g Add -10.   **h** Subtract -2.

When is it necessary to reverse the inequality sign to make the new inequality true?

10 Solve these inequalities.

  a $5 - 3x < 7$ **b** $-5 \leqslant 16 - 3x$

  c $4 - 3x \geqslant 22$ **d** $7 - 2x \leqslant -19$

  e $-2 - 3x \leqslant 10$ **f** $3 - 4x > 11 + x$

  g $5 - \dfrac{x}{2} > 0$

11 Solve these inequalities.

  a $5 - 6x < 29$ **b** $8 - 3x \geqslant 14$

  c $12 - 5x \geqslant 3$ **d** $8 + \dfrac{x}{2} > 11$

  e $5(x - 2) < 10$ **f** $6x + 7 > 8x + 15$

  g $\dfrac{x}{2} - 5 < x + 4$

12 There are mistakes in each of these solutions to inequalities.
Copy and correct them.

  a

$$5 - 3x < 14$$

Take 5 from both sides $-3x < 9$

Divide by -3 $x < -3$

  b

$$5(2 - x) \leqslant 25$$

Divide by 5 $2 - x \leqslant 5$

Subtract by 2 $-x \leqslant 3$

Multiply by -1 $x \leqslant -3$

13 The shaded region of the graph is formed by the lines $x = 4$, $y = 6$ and $y = x$.

Write three inequalities that describe this region.

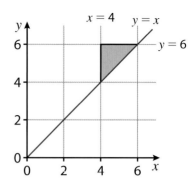

Wider skills practice

1 Copy these pairs of numbers and put the correct inequality sign between them.

a $\frac{3}{4}$ ☐ $\frac{3}{5}$ **b** -7 ☐ -4 **c** 0.8 ☐ $\frac{8}{9}$ **d** 0.1^2 ☐ 0.2^2

e $7\frac{3}{4}$ ☐ 7.7 **f** $(-2)^2$ ☐ -2 **g** -9 ☐ -0.9 **h** $\sqrt{6}$ ☐ 3

2 a Amy buys two chocolate bars from a vending machine.
  She puts in a £2 coin and receives some change.
  Let b stand for the cost, in pence, of a chocolate bar.
  Write this information as an inequality and solve it to
  find the price of a chocolate bar.

  b One lane on a small car ferry is 70m long.
  One metre must be left at each end of a lane for safety.
  The length allowed for one car is 5m.

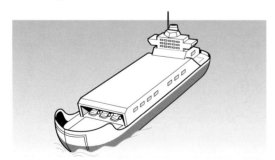

    i Let c be the number of cars in a lane. What is the inequality that defines c?

    ii What is the maximum number of cars that can fit into the lane?

Applying skills

1 Steve makes kitchen tables.

He always tries to make them 1500 mm long and 800 mm wide, but sometimes he does not cut the wood very accurately.
He measures all the table tops, in millimetres, to check the measurements. He writes down what he finds as inequalities.

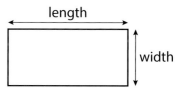

$1495 \leqslant$ length $\leqslant 1505$

$795 \leqslant$ width $\leqslant 805$

a Find the maximum and minimum area of a table in mm².

b Find the maximum and minimum area of a table in m².

Reviewing skills

1 Copy these pairs of numbers.
Put the correct inequality sign between them.
  a 3 ☐ 5
  b 0.1 ☐ 0.25
  c –5 ☐ –2
  d 2 ☐ –10

2 Let h be the height of an applicant.
Write this statement using inequalities.
Test pilot applicants must be between 160 cm and 180 cm inclusive.

3 Show each of these inequalities on a separate number line.
  a $x > 2$ **b** $-4 \leqslant x \leqslant 3$ **c** $-2 < x \leqslant 4$

4 Solve these inequalities.
  a $3x < 15$ **b** $2x + 5 \geqslant 17$ **c** $4x - 6 \leqslant 38$
  d $\frac{x}{3} + 4 > 24$ **e** $2 - 6x < 14$ **f** $2(x + 4) < 3x + 1$

Unit 3 • Solve pairs of equations by substitution • Band h

Building skills

Example outside the Maths classroom

Best tariffs

Toolbox

You can use the **substitution method** to solve this pair of **simultaneous equations**.

$$x + y = 6 \quad \text{(1)}$$
$$2x + y = 10 \quad \text{(2)}$$

- Make one of the unknowns the subject of equation (1):

$$y = 6 - x$$

- Substitute this into equation (2):

$$2x + 6 - x = 10 \quad \longleftarrow \boxed{\textbf{Solve to find } x.}$$
$$x + 6 = 10$$
$$x = 4$$

- Make sure you find the value of both unknowns by substituting the found value into the other equation, in this case equation (1):

$$4 + y = 6,$$
$$\text{so } y = 2$$

- Substitute the values back into equation (2) to check your answer:

$$2 \times 4 + 2 = 10 \checkmark$$

Example – Solving simultaneous equations using the substitution method

Solve these simultaneous equations using the substitution method.

$$y = 3x - 8$$
$$y = 12 - x$$

Solution

$$y = 3x - 8 \quad \text{(1)}$$
$$y = 12 - x \quad \text{(2)}$$

$$3x - 8 = 12 - x \quad \longleftarrow \boxed{\text{As both equations equal } y, \text{ they are equal to each other.}}$$
$$4x - 8 = 12 \quad \longleftarrow \boxed{\text{Add } x \text{ to both sides.}}$$
$$4x = 20 \quad \longleftarrow \boxed{\text{Add 8 to both sides.}}$$
$$x = 5 \quad \longleftarrow \boxed{\text{Divide both sides by 4.}}$$

$$y = 3x - 8 \quad ①$$
$$y = 3 \times 5 - 8$$
$$y = 15 - 8$$
$$y = 7$$

> Substitute the value of x you have just found into either equation to find y.

Check: $\quad y = 12 - x \quad ②$

$$7 = 12 - 5 \checkmark$$

So the solution is $x = 5$, $y = 7$.

> You need the values of both x and y for the solution.

Check: $\quad y = 12 - x \quad ②$

> Check your solution by substituting into the equation you didn't use to find y.

$$7 = 12 - 5$$

$$7 = 7 \checkmark$$

Example – Solving a word problem involving simultaneous equations

At the local shop, birthday cards cost five times as much as postcards.
John buys three birthday cards and six postcards.
The shopkeeper charges him £8.40.
How much does each birthday card and postcard cost?

Solution

Let b stand for the cost of a birthday card in pence.
Let c stand for the cost of a postcard in pence.

$$b = 5c \quad ①$$
$$3b + 6c = 840 \quad ②$$

> Birthday cards cost five times as much as postcards.

> Three birthday cards and six postcards cost 840 pence.

$$3b + 6c = 840 \quad ②$$
$$3 \times 5c + 6c = 840$$
$$15c + 6c = 840$$
$$21c = 840$$
$$c = 40$$

> Substitute this value of b ($5c$) into equation ②.

> Solve the equation to find c.

$$b = 5c \quad ①$$
$$b = 5 \times 40$$
$$= 200$$

> Substitute the value you found for c into equation ① to find b.

So a birthday card costs £2 and a postcard costs 40 pence.

> Write 200 pence as £2 in your solution.

Remember:

✦ You need to find both variables.

✦ Check your work by substituting into the other equation.

Skills practice A

1 Solve these simultaneous equations.

a $a = 3b$
$a = b + 2$

b $b = c + 1$
$b = 2c$

c $c = 5d$
$c = 3d + 4$

d $d = 2e$
$d = 5e - 6$

e $e = 2f$
$e = f + 4$

f $f = 2g - 1$
$f = 5g - 7$

2 Solve these simultaneous equations.

a $y = x$
$x + 3y = 12$

b $a = b$
$6b + a = 28$

c $g = 2h$
$g + 3h = 15$

d $m = 2n$
$2m + 2n = 12$

e $c = d + 3$
$c + 2d = 21$

f $f = 5 - e$
$3e + f = 9$

3 Solve these simultaneous equations.

a $s = t + 1$
$s + t = 7$

b $t = u + 3$
$t + u = 11$

c $u = v - 2$
$u + v = 8$

d $v = 2w$
$3w + 2v = 35$

e $w = x - 1$
$2x + 2w = 34$

f $x = 3y + 2$
$2x + 2y = 12$

g $y = 2z - 5$
$2y - z = 2$

Skills practice B

1 Solve these simultaneous equations.

a $y = x$
$2x + y = 9$

b $g = 2h$
$g + 4h = 18$

c $c = 3d$
$2c = 3 + 5d$

d $a = 2b + 1$
$2b + a = 11$

e $y = 3x + 5$
$y = 2x + 8$

f $r = 2s$
$s + 3r = 35$

g $2j = 3k - 1$
$4j + k = 5$

h $3r - 2s$
$4s - 12 = 12 - 6r$

2 Solve these pairs of simultaneous equations.

a $a + b = 3$
  $a = b + 1$

b $s = t + 3$
  $s + t = 5$

c $h = 2k - 4$
  $3h + k = 9$

d $x + y = 4$
  $2x - y = 5$

e $a - 2b = 1$
  $3a - 4b = 1$

f $3c + 2d = 10$
  $4c - d = 6$

g $5a + b = 0$
  $3a - 2b = 13$

h $4s = t + 7$
  $3s + 4t + 9 = 0$

3 Oliver thinks of two numbers.

One of my numbers is double the other. The sum of my two numbers is 15.

a Write down two equations for Oliver's numbers, using a and b to represent his two numbers.

b Solve your equations to find Oliver's numbers.

4 Susan thinks of two numbers.

The sum of two numbers is 24. The difference between them is 6.

a Write down two equations for Susan's numbers, using a and b to represent her two numbers.

b Solve your equations to find Susan's numbers.

5 Jane wants to buy some books with her birthday money.

I am buying three paperbacks and one hardback for £30

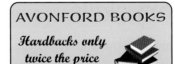

AVONFORD BOOKS

Hardbacks only twice the price of paperbacks!

a Write down an equation for what Jane buys using p for the price of a paperback book and h for the price of a hardback.

b Jane writes down the following equation.

$h = 2p$

What does it mean?

c Solve the two equations to find the price of each type of book.

6 At a pet shop, the price of four budgies and three goldfish is £41.
The four budgies cost £23 more than the three goldfish.
Find the price of each pet individually.

7 A news programme is 25 minutes longer than its subsequent weather forecast.
Combined, the news programme and weather forecast last for 32 minutes.
  a How long is the weather forecast?
  b How long is the news programme?

Wider skills practice

1 The perimeter of the rectangle is 10 cm.
The perimeter of the triangle is 7 cm.

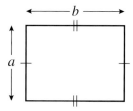 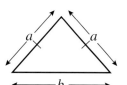

  a Write down an equation for the perimeter of the rectangle.
  b Write down an equation for the perimeter of the triangle.
  c Solve your two equations to find the dimensions of the rectangle.
  d How can you check that your solution is correct?

Applying skills

1 a A field contains some farmers and some sheep.
  How many of each are there in each of these cases?
   i There are 6 legs and 2 heads.
   ii There are 10 legs and 3 heads.
   iii There are 30 legs and 8 heads.
   iv There are 30 legs and 9 heads.
   v There are 50 legs and 15 heads.
   vi There are 50 legs and 14 heads.
   vii There are 50 legs and 13 heads.

  b Is it possible for the field in part a to contain 50 legs and 12 heads?
  c Find more impossible pairings of legs and heads.
  (Assume all the farmers have two legs and all the sheep have four legs.)

Reviewing skills

1 Solve these equations by substitution.

   a $y = x$
      $x + 4y = 25$

   b $a = 5b$
      $2a + 3b = 52$

   c $5d - 2e + 14 = 0$
      $5e = d + 12$

2 Kate is thinking of two numbers.
   Call them m and n.

   a Write down two equations for m and n.
   b Solve your equations to find the two numbers.
   c How can you check that your answer is correct?
   d Are there other possible answers for m and n?

When my two numbers are added together the answer is 21.

The difference between my two numbers is 3.

Building skills

Example outside the Maths classroom

Best tariffs

Toolbox

A pair of simultaneous equations can be solved by **eliminating** one of the unknowns.

You either **add or subtract the equations** to form a third equation in just one unknown.

* To decide whether to add or subtract look at the signs of the unknown you wish to eliminate.
  If the signs are different, you add.
  If the signs are the same, you subtract.
* Sometimes you need to multiply each term in one (or both) equations by a constant so that one of the unknowns have the same coefficients.

When you have found one unknown, substitute in either equation to find the other.

To check your answer, substitute the values you have found into both equations.

Example – Subtracting simultaneous equations

Solve these simultaneous equations.

$$5x + 3y = 18$$
$$5x - 2y = 13$$

Solution

$$5x + 3y = 18 \quad \text{①}$$
$$\underline{5x - 2y = 13} \quad \text{②}$$

Subtract $\quad 0 + 5y = 5$

$$y = 1$$

> Both equations have $5x$, so you can eliminate x.

> The signs in front of both $5x$ are the same ($+5x$) so you subtract.

> Divide both sides by 5.

Alternatively,

$$5x + 3y = 18 \quad \text{①}$$
$$\underline{-5x + 2y = -13} \quad \text{②}$$

Add $\quad 0 + 5y = 5$

> When subtracting one equation from another, you may find it helps to change the signs in the second equation and then add.

① $5x + 3y = 18$

$5x + 3 \times 1 = 18$ ←   To find x, substitute $y = 1$ into equation ①.

$5x + 3 = 18$ ←   Subtract 3 from both sides.

$5x = 15$ ←   Divide both sides by 5.

$x = 3$

So the solution is $x = 3$ and $y = 1$.

Check: $5x + 3y = 18$ ① $5x - 2y = 13$ ②

$5 \times 3 + 3 \times 1 = 18$ $5 \times 3 - 2 \times 1 = 13$

$15 + 3 = 18$ $15 - 2 = 13$

$18 = 18 \checkmark$ $13 = 13 \checkmark$

Example – Multiplying simultaneous equations by a constant

Solve these simultaneous equations.

$3s + 2t = 13$

$5s - t = 13$

Solution

$3s + 2t = 13$ ①

$5s - t = 13$ ②   ←   Multiply equation ② by 2 to eliminate t.

① $3s + 2t = 13$

② × 2 $\underline{10s - 2t = 26}$ ←   The signs in front of the $2t$ are different ($+2t$ and $-2t$) so you add.

Add $13s + 0 = 39$

$s = \dfrac{39}{13}$ ←   Divide both sides by 13.

$s = 3$

① $3s + 2t = 13$

$3 \times 3 + 2t = 13$ ←   To find t, substitute $s = 3$ into equation ①

$9 + 2t = 13$ ←   Subtract 9 from both sides.

$2t = 4$

$t = 2$ ←   Divide both sides by 2.

So the solution is $s = 3$ and $t = 2$.

Check: $3s + 2t = 13$ ① $5s - t = 13$ ②

$3 \times 3 + 2 \times 2 = 13$ $5 \times 3 - 2 = 13$

$9 + 4 = 13$ $15 - 2 = 13$

$13 = 13 \checkmark$ $13 = 13 \checkmark$

Example – Solving a word problem using simultaneous equations

Danni has £4.40 in 2p and 5p coins.
She has 100 coins altogether.
Write down two equations for this information.
How many of each type of coin does she have?

Solution

Let t = number of 2p coins and $\longleftarrow$ | Choose letters to represent the unknowns.
f = number of 5p coins.

$t + f = 100$ (1) $\longleftarrow$ | There are 100 coins altogether.

$2t + 5f = 440$ (2) $\longleftarrow$ | Danni has 440 pence altogether. This matches the 2 and 5 which are in pence.

$5 \times$ (1) $5t + 5f = 500$ $\longleftarrow$ | Make the coefficients of one of the unknowns the same in both equations.

(2) $2t + 5f = 440$ $\longleftarrow$ | The signs on $5f$ are positive in both equations, so subtract.

Subtract $3t + 0 = 60$

$t = \dfrac{60}{3}$ $\longleftarrow$ | Divide both sides by 3.

$t = 20$

(1) $t + f = 100$ $\longleftarrow$ | To find f, substitute $t = 20$ into equation (1).

$20 + f = 100$

$f = 80$

So Danni has 20 two-pence coins and 80 five-pence coins.

Check: $t + f = 100$ (1) $2t + 5f = 440$ (2)

$20 + 80 = 100$ $2 \times 20 + 5 \times 80 = 440$

$100 = 100$ ✓ $40 + 400 = 440$ ✓

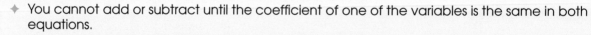

Remember:

✦ You cannot add or subtract until the coefficient of one of the variables is the same in both equations.

✦ Take extra care when subtracting one equation from another.

✦ Always check your answers by substituting your solution back into both the original equations.

Skills practice A

1 Copy and complete this solution.

    ① $4x + 5y = 22$

    ② $6x - 5y = 8$

Add $10x + 0 = \square$

          $10x = \square$

            $x = \square$

Substitute $x = \square$ into equation ①

      $4x + 5y = 22$

$4 \times \square + 5y = 22$

    $\square + 5y = 22$

        $5y = \square$

         $y = \square$

Solution: $x = \square$ and $y = \square$

Now check your answer.

2 Look at this pair of simultaneous equations.

$$2p + 4q = 14$$
$$p - 4q = 1$$

a What does $3p$ equal?

b What are the values of p and q?

3 Simplify these expressions.

a $3x - 5x$

b $2x + (-2x)$

c $2x - (-2x)$

d $(-5x) - (-5x)$

4 Solve these simultaneous equations by adding the two equations.

a $4x + y = 12$
    $3x - y = 2$

b $2x + y = 12$
    $x - y = 3$

c $14x - 3y = 43$
    $2x + 3y = 37$

d $3x + y = 18$
    $x - y = 2$

e $x - y = 2$
    $3x + y = 18$

f $4x + 2y = 28$
    $x - 2y = 2$

5 Solve these simultaneous equations by subtracting one from the other.

a $4a + 3b = 13$
    $2a + 3b = 11$

b $3x + 5y = 29$
    $3x + 3y = 21$

c $5p + 4r = 23$
    $3p + 4r = 17$

d $8c + 4d = 28$
    $6c + 4d = 26$

e $5s + 3t = 41$
    $5s + 6t = 47$

f $12f + 4g = 36$
    $12f + 6g = 42$

6 Copy and complete this solution.

Solve $2x + 3y = 12$ ①

        $x - y = 1$ ②

         ① $2x + 3y = 12$

$3 \times$ ② $3x - 3y = \square$

Add $\square = 15$

         $x = \square$

Substitute $x = \square$ into equation ①

     $2x + 3y = 12$

$2 \times \square + 3y = 12$

   $\square + 3y = 12$

       $3y = 12 - \square$

       $3y = \square$

        $y = \square$

Solution: $x = \square$ and $y = \square$

7 Solve these simultaneous equations.

a $6x - 3y = 12$
    $4x - 3y = 6$

b $3a + 6b = 24$
    $3a + 4b = 18$

c $3e + 2f = 10$
    $3e - f = 4$

d $4m + 2n = 34$
    $6m - 2n = 16$

e $6s - 2t = 0$
    $4s - 2t = 0$

f $5x - 2y = 8$
    $7x + 2y = 16$

Skills practice B

1 Solve these simultaneous equations.

a $7j - 3k = 19$
    $7j + k = 31$

b $4s - 2t = 22$
    $2s - 2t = 8$

c $12a - 4b = 4$
    $10a - 4b = 2$

d $6f - 4g = 32$
    $6f + 2g = 38$

e $4m + 2n = 14$
    $4m + 7n = 19$

f $2a + 3b = 7$
    $2a - b = 3$

2 Solve these simultaneous equations.

a $2x + 3y = 5$
    $x + y = 2$

b $4x - y = 3$
    $x + 2y = 11$

c $5x - 7y = 8$
    $x + y = 12$

d $4x + y = 8$
    $x + 3y = 2$

e $2x + 3y = 11$
    $x + 6y = 10$

f $5x - 2y = 3$
    $x + 4y = 5$

3 Solve these simultaneous equations.

a $3a + 2b = 13$
    $5a + 4b = 23$

b $2c + 3d = 17$
    $6c + 4d = 26$

c $4m - 6n = 4$
    $3m + 2n = 29$

d $4p - 2r = 12$
    $8p - 5r = 22$

e $2f + 3g = 21$
    $6f - 4g = 24$

f $2s - t = 5$
    $5s - 4t = 11$

4 Solve these simultaneous equations.

    a $6x - 3y = 3$
          $2x + 5y = 7$

    b $5j + 2k = 45$
          $3j + 6k = 75$

    c $2e - 3f = 10$
          $6e + f = 130$

    d $2m - 5n = 1$
          $5m + 3n = 49$

    e $5a + b = 11$
          $3a + 4b = 10$

    f $2x + y = 100$
          $x - 2y = 45$

5 To solve these simultaneous equations you will need to multiply both of them by suitable numbers before you add or subtract.

    a $3s - 2t = 4$
          $5s + 3t = 13$

    b $2a - 3b = 2$
          $3a - 2b = 8$

    c $4x + 3y = 11$
          $5x - 2y = 8$

    d $50x + 2y = 102$
          $3x + 7y = 13$

    e $3x - 4y = 0$
          $2x + 7y = 29$

6 Amy buys three lollipops and one bar of chocolate for 65p.

    Beth buys one lollipop and one bar of chocolate for 35p.

    a Write down an equation for what Amy buys using l pence for the cost of a lollipop and c pence for the cost of a bar of chocolate.

    b Write down an equation for what Beth buys.

    c Work out the cost of a lollipop and the cost of a bar of chocolate.

7 Dan buys four candles and two rockets.

    He spends £52.

    a Write an equation for what Dan buys using c for the cost of a candle and r for the cost of a rocket.

    b Nesrene buys one candle and two rockets. She spends £22.

    Write down a second equation in terms of c and r.

    c Solve your simultaneous equations to find the cost of one candle and the cost of one rocket.

Fireworks
Special offer on all candles and rockets !

8   **a** Cynthia buys two ballpoint pens and four pencils for £2.

    Write down an equation for what Cynthia buys using b pence for the cost of a ballpoint pen and p pence for the cost of a pencil. (**Hint**: Write 100 pence rather than £1.)

    b Darrell buys five ballpoint pens and four pencils for £3.80.

    Write down a second equation in terms of b and p.

    c Solve your simultaneous equations to find the cost of one ballpoint pen and the cost of one pencil.

9 Natalie buys three toffees and four chocolates for 76p.

    Scott buys nine toffees and two chocolates for £1.28.

    a Write down two equations for this information using t pence for the cost of a toffee and c pence for the cost of a chocolate.

    b Find the cost of one toffee and the cost of one chocolate.

10 A family of seven people go to the cinema.

    a There are a adults and c children. Write down an equation for this information.

    b The cinema trip costs £54. Write down a second equation in terms of a and c.

    c How many children go to the cinema?

PICK & MIX

AVONFORD CINEMA

Adults   £10
Children   £6

11 Daniel buys four mugs and five plates for £60.

Sarah buys eight mugs and two plates for £88.

   a Write down two equations for this information using m for the cost of a mug and p for the cost of a plate.

   b Find the cost of one mug and the cost of one plate.

Wider skills practice

1 The length of this rectangle is 10 cm and the width is 8 cm.

   a Write down two equations involving a and b.

   b Solve your equations simultaneously.

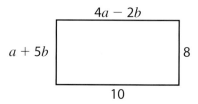

2 Dogs and cats can be boarded at East Dillwood Farm when their owners go on holiday.

One week East Dillwood Farm has three dogs and four cats and their total income is £469.

Another week they have five dogs and four cats and their total income is £623.

c is the cost of boarding a cat for one week

and d is the cost of boarding a dog for one week.

   a Write down two equations involving c and d.

      Solve your equations simultaneously to find the weekly cost of boarding a cat and of boarding a dog.

   b What is the cost per day of boarding a cat?

   c What is the cost per day of boarding a dog?

   d What is the total income when ten dogs and seven cats stay for three days?

3 A group of three adults and five children buy tickets at a theme park.

The total cost is £234.

A second group of five adults and six children spend £334.

   a Write down a pair of simultaneous equations.

      Solve your equations to find the cost of a ticket for an adult and of a ticket for a child.

   b A school party consists of six adults and 70 children.

      What is the cost of entry to the theme park for the school party?

   c One week there is a special offer for schools.

      One adult gets in free for every 12 children paid for.

      How much does it cost for a school party of six adults and 70 children to go to the theme park in that week?

Reasoning

4 Cycle hire is available at a country park for a daily charge.

The cost of hiring one tandem and two bicycles is £66.

The cost of hiring two tandems and five bicycles is £150.

a Write down a pair of simultaneous equations.

Solve your equations simultaneously to find the daily hire charge for a tandem and for a bicycle.

b Work out the cost of hiring individual bicycles for 11 people

c What is the lowest possible cost for these 11 people?

Applying skills

1 Mary works at Avonford Pet Rescue Centre.

One Saturday, she feeds each large dog six biscuits and each small dog four biscuits. There are 15 dogs altogether and between them they eat 80 biscuits.

How many large dogs are in the rescue centre?

2 A rail company is working out the new summer train timetable.

	Number of stops	Journey time (in minutes)
Slow train	23	143
Fast train	5	89

How much time does each stop add to the journey?

a Find out how long each stop takes.

b Find out how long the journey would be without any stops.

3 Jack thinks of a two-digit number.

Which two-digit number could Jack be thinking of?

The sum of the digits in my number is 10.
I can reverse the digits to make a second number.
The difference between my two numbers is 36.

Jack

4 Look at these arrays.

Each piece of fruit has been assigned a value.

For example, in part **a**, 3 apples + 2 bananas + 1 cherry = 13.

Work out the value of each piece of fruit. It is different in each array.

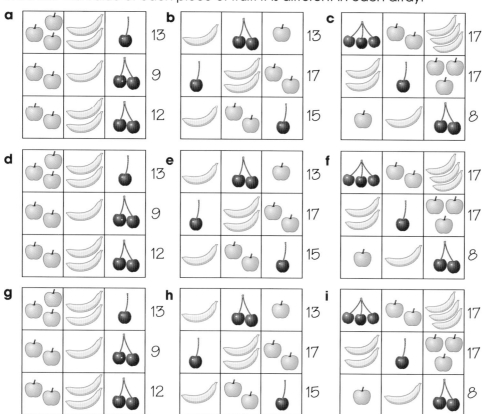

5 Solve these simultaneous equations.

a $3x + 2y - z = 5$
$2x + y + z = 8$
$x + 2y + 2z = 10$

b $x + y + z = 9$
$2x - y + 3z = 15$
$x + 2y - z = 5$

c How many equations would you need to find the value of five unknowns?

Reviewing skills

1 Solve these simultaneous equations.

  a $2x + y = 10$
     $x + y = 7$

  b $3a + 7b = 47$
     $3a + 4b = 32$

  c $5c + 2d = 23$
     $3c - 2d = 1$

  d $5x + 3y = 43$
     $2x + 3y = 28$

2 Solve these simultaneous equations.

  a $3x - 2y = -17$
     $5x + 2y = -7$

  b $2x + 3y = 19$
     $3x + 2y = 16$

  c $2x + 3y = 21$
     $4x - 2y = 2$

  d $6x - 4y = 36$
     $2x + 3y = -1$

3 Meena buys six mugs and four plates for £36.
  Susan buys four mugs and six plates for £34.

  a Write down two equations for this information using £m for the cost of a mug and £p for the cost of a plate.

  b Solve the equations to find the cost of one mug and the cost of one plate.

Building skills

Example outside the Maths classroom

Best tariffs

Toolbox

To solve these equations graphically:

$$y = 2x + 1$$
$$y = 4 - x$$

- Plot both equations on the same axes.

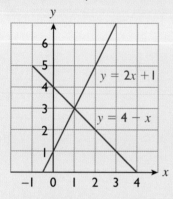

- If necessary, extend the lines so that they meet.
- Find the co-ordinates of the point where the two lines meet, in this case (1, 3).
- Make sure you write the solution as $x =$ and $y =$. In this case, the solution is $x = 1$ and $y = 3$.

Example – Solving simultaneous equations graphically

Solve these simultaneous equations using a graph.

$$y = 2x$$
$$y = 6 - 2x$$

Solution

x	0	1	3
$y = 2x$	0	2	6

x	0	1	3
6	6	6	6
$-2x$	0	-2	-6
$y = 6 - 2x$	6	4	0

> Find three points on each line.

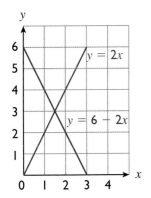

Plot the points for the two lines on the same graph.

The lines cross at the point (1.5, 3)

The solution is $x = 1.5$ and $y = 3$.

Remember:

✦ You only need two points to draw a straight line, but using three allows you to spot any errors.

Skills practice A

1 For each graph, write down the co-ordinates of the point where the lines intersect.

a

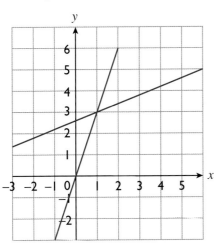

b

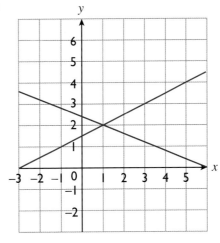

c

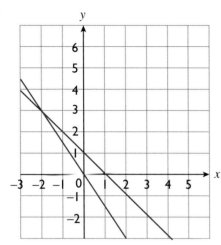

d

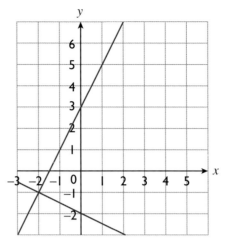

2 Here is a graph of the lines $y = 2x + 2$ and $y = 5 - x$.

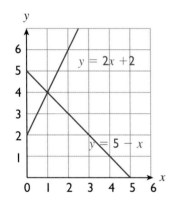

    a Write down the co-ordinates of the point where the two lines intersect.

    b Write down the solution of the simultaneous equations $y = 2x + 2$ and $y = 5 - x$.

3 Here is a graph of the lines $y = 2x - 5$ and $y = x - 1$.

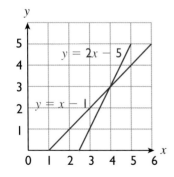

    a Write down the co-ordinates of the point where the two lines intersect.

    b Write down the solution of the simultaneous equations $y = 2x - 5$ and $y = x - 1$.

4 a Copy and complete this table.

x	0	1	2	3	4
$4x$	0			12	
-2	-2			-2	
$y = 4x - 2$	-2			10	

b Make a table for the line $y = 2x + 1$.
c Draw the lines $y = 4x - 2$ and $y = 2x + 1$ on the same axes.
d Use your graph to solve the simultaneous equations $y = 4x - 2$ and $y = 2x + 1$.

5 a Complete a table of values to find three points on these lines:

$y = 2x + 3$

$y = 6 - x$

$y = 7 - 2x$

$y = x + 1$

b Plot each line on the same graph.
c Use your graph to solve these four pairs of simultaneous equations:

i $y = 2x + 3$	**ii** $y = 6 - x$	**iii** $y = 6 - x$	**iv** $y = 7 - 2x$
$y = x + 1$	$y = x + 1$	$y = 7 - 2x$	$y = x + 1$

d State what other pairs of equations you can solve from your graph.
Give their solutions.

Skills practice B

1 a Copy and complete this table for the line $y = 4x - 10$.

x	0	1	2	3	4
$4x$			8		
-10			-10		
$y = 4x - 10$			-2		

b Complete a table for the line $y = 2x - 3$.
c Draw the lines $y = 4x - 10$ and $y = 2x - 3$ on the same axes.
d Use your graph to solve these simultaneous equations.

$y = 4x - 10$

$y = 2x - 3$

e Now add the line $y = 2x - 1$ to your graph.
Explain why the simultaneous equations:

$y = 2x - 1$

$y = 2x - 3$

do not have a solution.

2 a Draw and label a pair of axes numbered from −15 to 15 for both x and y.
Draw these lines on your graph.

$y = x$ $\qquad$ $y = 2x$ $\qquad$ $x + y = -3$ $\qquad$ $y = x - 3$ $\qquad$ $y = -2x + 1$

b Use your graph to solve these pairs of simultaneous equations.

i $y = 2x$ $\qquad$ **ii** $y = x - 3$ $\qquad$ **iii** $y = x$ $\qquad$ **iv** $y = 2x$
$\quad\ y = x$ $\qquad\qquad$ $x + y = -3$ $\qquad\quad$ $x + y = -3$ $\qquad\quad$ $y = x - 3$

c Use substitution to check your answers to part **b**.

3 a Try to solve the equations

$\qquad y = x$
$\qquad y = x - 3$

using algebra.
What happens?

b Now draw the lines $y = x$ and $y = x - 3$ on a graph.

c Explain what you found in part **a**.

4 Solve these simultaneous equations by drawing their graphs on the same axes.
Check your solution by substitution.

$\qquad y = x + 2$
$\qquad y = 2x - 5$

5 Solve these simultaneous equations by drawing their graphs on the same axes.
Check your solution by substitution.

$\qquad y = 3x$
$\qquad x + y = 8$

Wider skills practice

1 Look at this pair of simultaneous equations.

$\qquad 3x + y = 10$ $\quad$ ①
$\qquad x + y = 4$ $\qquad$ ②

You are going to solve them by three different methods.

a First use addition or subtraction to eliminate a variable.
Do not rearrange the equations.

b Now solve by writing equation ② as $y = 4 - x$ and substituting it into equation ①.

c Finally, make y the subject of both equations and solve them graphically.

d Which method did you find the quickest?

e For each method, explain how you can check your answers.

Reasoning

2 a Some of these pairs of simultaneous equations have no solution.
Which ones?
Explain your answers fully.

i $x + y = 5$
$3x + 3y = 16$

ii $y = x$
$y = 2x + 1$

iii $2y + 4x = 12$
$y = 6 - 2x$

iv $x + y = 10$
$y = 5 - x$

v $y = 2x - 1$
$y = 2x + 4$

vi $x + y = 10$
$y = 4x$

b Solve the remaining simultaneous equations.

Applying skills

1 Look at this graph.

Point of intersection (−1, 6)

Point of intersection (4, 6)

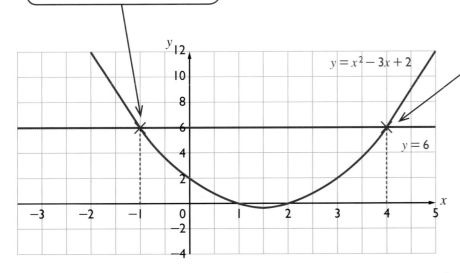

It shows the quadratic curve $y = x^2 - 3x + 2$ and the straight line $y = 6$.
They intersect at the points $(-1, 6)$ and $(4, 6)$.
So the solutions of the simultaneous equations
$$y = x^2 - 3x + 2 \text{ and } y = 6$$
are $x = -1, y = 6$ and $x = 4, y = 6$.
Copy the graph of $y = x^2 - 3x + 2$.

Draw suitable lines on it to solve these simultaneous equations.

a $y = x^2 - 3x + 2$
$y = 2$

b $y = x^2 - 3x + 2$
$y = 12$

c $y = x^2 - 3x + 2$
$y = 2 - x$

Reviewing skills

1 a On the same pair of axes, draw the graphs of $y = 3x$ and $y = 8 - x$ for values of x from 0 to 10.

   b Use your graph to solve these simultaneous equations.

   $y = 3x$
   $y = 8 - x$

2 Some pairs of simultaneous equations have no solution.

   a Find a pair of equations that have no solution. Explain how you know.

   b What happens if you draw their graphs?